COMPASSION

Person of Jesus: A Study of Love

PARTICIPANT'S MANUAL

Unit One

PAUL E. MILLER

seeJesus®

a global discipling mission

Person of Jesus, Unit One: Compassion (Participant's Manual)

Published by seeJesus Press
P.O. Box 197, Telford, PA 18969
Phone: 215.721.3113
info@seeJesus.net
www.seeJesus.net

The mission of seeJesus is to help people see and reflect the life, death, and resurrection of Jesus through our discipleship resources and training.

Author: Paul E. Miller
Editor: Michele Walton
Proofreaders: Steve Bohannon, Sherri Hughes, and Lydia Leggett
Layout design: Pat Reinheimer and Seth Guge
Cover design: Mary Ann Martin

Scripture quotations marked AT are the author's translation.

ISBN 978-1-941178-31-7

Dedication

I know no one who has worked longer or harder than
Tim Strawbridge to help the church see the person of Jesus.
Thanks, Timo, for helping us see Jesus!

Thank you to Howard and Deanna Bayless for making
the rewrite of *Person of Jesus* possible.

CONTENTS

INTRODUCTION

This five-part small group study introduces a Jesus so personal, so rich in love, that you will be captivated heart-first. Paul Miller's winsome insights—conveyed through an energetic, interactive format—will lead you to discover Jesus' beauty for yourself. In watching Jesus, you will find your eyes opened to a rich encounter with God's love and your heart empowered to love others.

This interactive study is divided into five units. Since the concepts build upon one another, it is ideal to go through it in sequence. For example, the more you study compassion (Unit One), the more you wonder what the boundaries of compassion are. Units Two and Three (*Honesty* and *Dependence*) provide those boundaries. Finally, the last two units show us what love leads to (oneness) and what the journey entails (humility, sadness, and joy).

Unit One: Compassion

We watch Jesus interact with people to discover the three steps of love: to look, feel compassion, and act.

Unit Two: Honesty

We study how Jesus relates to different people during meals to find that a commitment to truth and justice must balance compassion.

Unit Three: Dependence

We see how Jesus' dependence on his Father, rooted in a deep understanding of Scripture and a life of prayer, shapes all of his relationships and allows him to say no to others' attempts to control him.

Unit Four: Faith

Are compassion, honesty, and dependence enough? Jesus reveals to his disciples how faith in God gives us the energy to love.

Unit Five: The Passion

Death is at the heart of love. The final unit of *Person of Jesus* traces Jesus' journey to the cross and shows how, in the low place of humility, we learn to see clearly because God lives there.

UNIT ONE: COMPASSION

SUMMARY

When Jesus is confronted with suffering, he looks, feels compassion, and then acts. This pattern may be found not only in Jesus' life but also in his teaching. The Good Samaritan looks, feels compassion, and then helps. The father of the Lost Son looks for his son, feels compassion, and then runs to greet him.

Jesus' act of looking is featured in numerous Gospel stories. For instance, in the home of Simon the Pharisee, Jesus teaches Simon to look by turning toward the adulterous woman and asking Simon, "Do you see this woman?" (Luke 7:36-50).

Three enemies of compassion are judging, self-righteousness, and legalism. The story in John 9 of the blind man is a study in judging versus looking. Jesus and the disciples are walking together, but only Jesus looks at the man; the disciples simply judge him.

We conclude Unit One by seeing that Jesus' love follows the pattern of his incarnation. Love *incarnates*—goes inside the world of the person being loved. The Golden Rule is an invitation to incarnation.

LESSON 1: COMPASSION

OUTLINE:

1. The Funeral . . . . 10 mins
2. The Steps of Love . . . . 25 mins
3. Summary . . . . 10 mins

LESSON 1: COMPASSION

SECTION 1: The Funeral 10 mins

Luke 7:11-12

[11] Soon afterward, Jesus went to a town called Nain, and his disciples and a large crowd went along with him. [12] As he approached the town gate, a dead person was being carried out—the only son of his mother, and she was a widow. And a large crowd from the town was with her.

1. Think about a typical American funeral. What kinds of things do you see and hear?

Historical Background: First-century Jewish Funeral[1]

- Jewish funeral rites, both ancient and modern, require a body to be buried within 24 hours.
- First-century Jewish funerals, like modern American ones, move the bodies of the dead to the place of burial in processions. But Jewish processions are loud and emotional, accompanied by mourning women and flute players.

---

1 Alfred Edersheim, *The Life and Times of Jesus the Messiah*, vol. 1 (Grand Rapids, MI: Eerdmans, 1971), 552-559. See also Alfred Edersheim, *Sketches of Jewish Social Life* (Peabody, MA: Hendrickson Publishers, 1994), 148ff.

- Even a poor Jewish family is expected to have one mourning woman and two flute players. Amos 5:16 and Jeremiah 9:17 mention those "skilled in mourning."
- As the procession begins, the body is placed face-up, with hands folded, in an open wicker basket. In the Galilee region, women lead the procession because it is believed they brought death into the world. Pallbearers frequently change hands, so that many can bear the burden.
- There are no flowers because flowers would later be introduced by Christians to symbolize the resurrection.

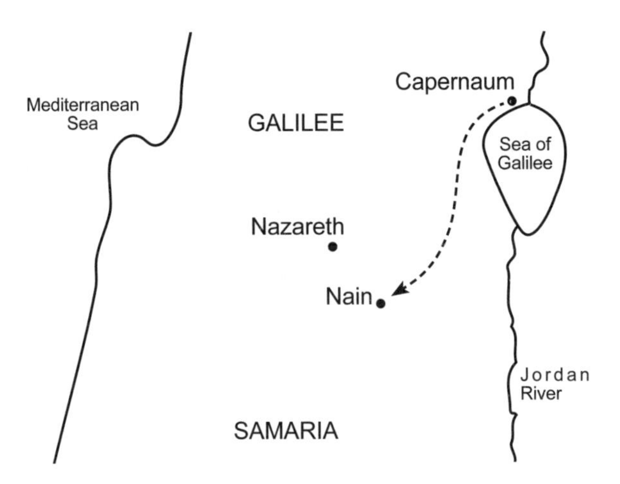

- The Setting: Nain is nestled into the southern hillside overlooking the beautiful Jezreel Valley. "Nain" sounds like the Hebrew word for "pleasant." Jacob's promise to his son Issachar, whose tribe settled in the region, is that "he sees how pleasant is his land" (Genesis 49:15).
- The Time: Funerals are usually in early evening, around 6 PM. Jesus' 25-mile journey from Capernaum puts him in Nain around the same time.
- The Crowds: Nain's entire population of between 300 and 500 people are expected to attend this funeral, so it's no surprise the Greek text calls the funeral crowd "considerable." Jesus' crowd, however, is "a great multitude"—the same word used at the feeding of the 5,000. His crowd is likely 1,000 to 2,000 people.

Luke 7:13-17

[13] When the Lord saw her, his heart went out to her and he said, "Don't cry."

[14] Then he went up and touched the bier they were carrying him on, and the bearers stood still. He said, "Young man, I say to you, get up!" [15] The dead man sat up and began to talk, and Jesus gave him back to his mother.

[16] They were all filled with awe and praised God. "A great prophet has appeared among us," they said. "God has come to help his people." [17] This news about Jesus spread throughout Judea and the surrounding country.

2. How does Jesus love the widow?

SECTION 2: The Steps of Love 25 mins

1ST: JESUS LOOKS—"WHEN THE LORD SAW HER..." (7:13)

3. What could Jesus be looking at instead of the widow? What would you be looking at?

4. Considering the size of the crowd and that someone notices his gaze, how is Jesus likely looking at the widow?

2ND: COMPASSION—"...HIS HEART WENT OUT TO HER" (7:13)

5. This question is so simple that it can be hard to answer: how do we know Jesus felt compassion?

6. Read Luke 1:1-3 with me. Did Luke see this event directly, or did he interview an eyewitness?

7. How did the eyewitness know Jesus felt compassion?

Insight: Jesus' Compassion

"The emotion which we should naturally expect to find most frequently attributed to Jesus whose whole life was a mission of mercy, and whose ministry was so marked by deeds of benevolence that it was summed up in the memory of his followers as a going through the land 'doing good' (Acts 10:38), is no doubt 'compassion.' In point of fact, this is the emotion which is most frequently attributed to him." —B.B. Warfield[2]

8. Compassion can be hard to visualize. For comparison's sake, let's visualize anger first. What do you see, feel, or hear when someone is angry?

9. Compassion is subtle, but it still has physical expressions. What do you see, feel, or hear when someone is showing compassion?

[2] Benjamin Breckenridge Warfield, "The Emotional Life of Our Lord," in *The Person and Work of Christ* (Philadelphia, PA: Presbyterian and Reformed Publishing Company, 1951), 97.

ANGER	COMPASSION

10. When you feel compassion, where are you going emotionally? Physically?

11. Let's consider why Jesus feels compassion. What has the widow lost?

Historical Background: The Death of a Son

Having a son meant everything in ancient Near Eastern culture. When the prophet Jeremiah tells Jerusalem how to weep for their besieged city, he says: "O my people, put on sackcloth and roll in ashes; mourn with bitter wailing as for an only son, for suddenly the destroyer will come upon us" (Jeremiah 6:26).

Historical Background: A Living Death

We think of death and life as distinct categories, but in Hebrew thought there was an in-between state—a person could be considered half-dead. In the Old Testament, when Naomi returns home after burying her husband and two sons, she says to the townspeople: "Do not call me Naomi ['pleasant'], call me Bitter, because God has made my life very bitter" (Ruth 1:20). Naomi was alive but felt dead. So when you greeted Naomi on the street you would say, "Hi, Bitter." The widow of Nain, like Naomi, has entered into a living death, cut off from Israel.

3rd: Comfort—"...and he said, 'Do not cry'" (7:13)

12. Why does Jesus tell her not to cry?

Insight:
Picture a 3-year-old boy running to his mom, wailing because he scraped his knee. His mom hugs him and says, "Don't cry. It's going to be okay." She knows the wound will soon heal, and the pain will go away. Her words bring hope. That's what Jesus is doing. He feels her pain, but he's not given over emotionally to her circumstances. He can anchor himself in a future reality and help her to do the same. It is going to be okay.

4TH: HELPING—"'YOUNG MAN, I SAY TO YOU, GET UP!'" (7:13)

13. How does Jesus stop the procession?

14. If Jesus needs to stop it, what has the procession been doing until this point?

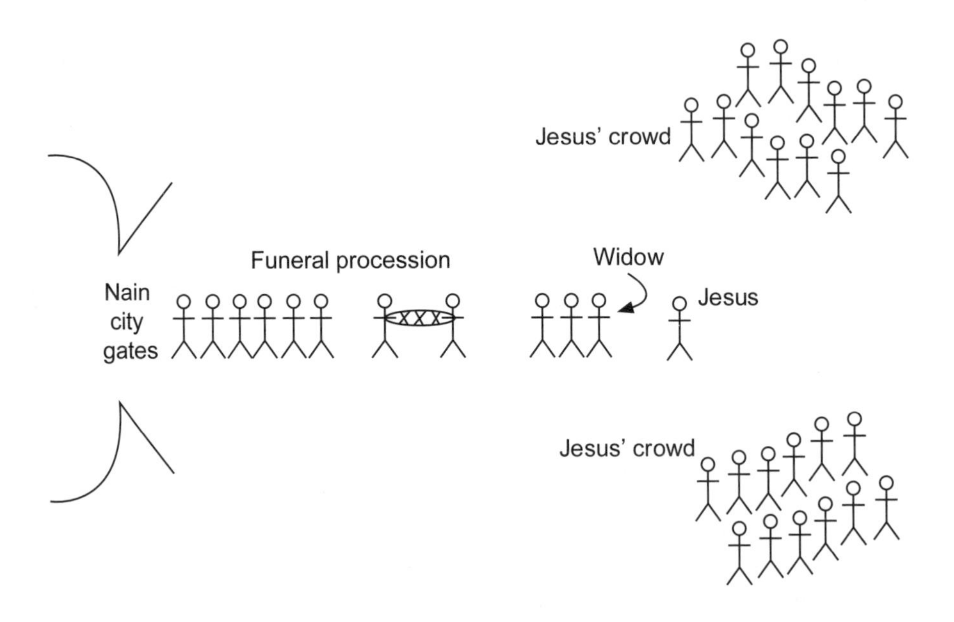

15. What does Jesus' method of stopping the procession tell you about him as a person?

Insight:
In Isaiah 42:3, the prophet says the Messiah will be so gentle he won't break a bruised reed or put out a smoldering wick. He will be so tender that when he holds an oil lamp whose wick is barely lit, he won't blow it out.

16. What would have surprised a first-century Jew about Jesus touching the casket?

17. If this was the first time you saw Jesus, what would strike you about him as a person?

Insight:

The American theologian Jonathan Edwards said the essence of the beauty of Jesus is that he combines characteristics not normally seen in one person: justice and mercy, glory and humility, authority and gentleness. He is both the Lion and the Lamb.[3]

5TH: FOCUS ON THE PERSON—"…JESUS GAVE HIM BACK TO HIS MOTHER" (7:13)

18. Which two people is the crowd thinking about now?

19. What does the crowd call Jesus?

Historical Background: A Prophet

Nain is about three miles from where Elisha raised the only son of a couple at Shunem (2 Kings 4:8-37). The last time God raised someone from the dead, it was an only son—just a few miles from this spot. So, this miracle points to an Elisha-like prophet from God. After 400 years without a prophet in the land to bring the Word of God, the crowd immediately thinks, "God has finally visited his people."[4]

---

[3] Jonathan Edwards, "The Excellency of Christ," in *The Sermons of Jonathan Edwards, A Reader* (New Haven, CT: Yale University Press, 1999), 161-196.

[4] Two hundred years earlier (in the time of the Maccabees), after Antiochus Epiphanes polluted the altar by sacrificing a pig on it, the priests wondered if they could use the defiled altar stones. Since there was no prophet to tell them what to do, "they tore down the altar and stored the stones in a convenient place on the temple hill until there should come a prophet" (I Maccabees 4:45-46). First Maccabees is not a book of the Bible, yet like the writings of Josephus, it is useful for understanding historical context.

20. After the miracle, the crowd is thinking about Jesus and God. But who is Jesus thinking about?

21. How do we know Jesus is thinking about the woman?

22. Whom does Jesus go to first? Second? Last?

Son **Widow** **Jesus**

23. Who is at the physical center of Jesus' love?

Insight: The Balance of Love

- Jesus models a balance between focusing on the person and focusing on the project.
- The compassion Jesus feels shapes the way he performs the miracle. By first focusing on and feeling for her as a person, rather than seeing her as a project or a stepping-stone, he is able to make her central to the miracle itself.

24. Why does Jesus give the son back to his mother? It seems unnecessary.

25. Why doesn't Jesus preach a sermon? What does this tell you about him?

SECTION 3: Summary 10 mins

26. Based on how Jesus loved the widow, what are the three steps of love? What was the first thing Jesus did? Second? Can you give me one word to summarize everything else he did?

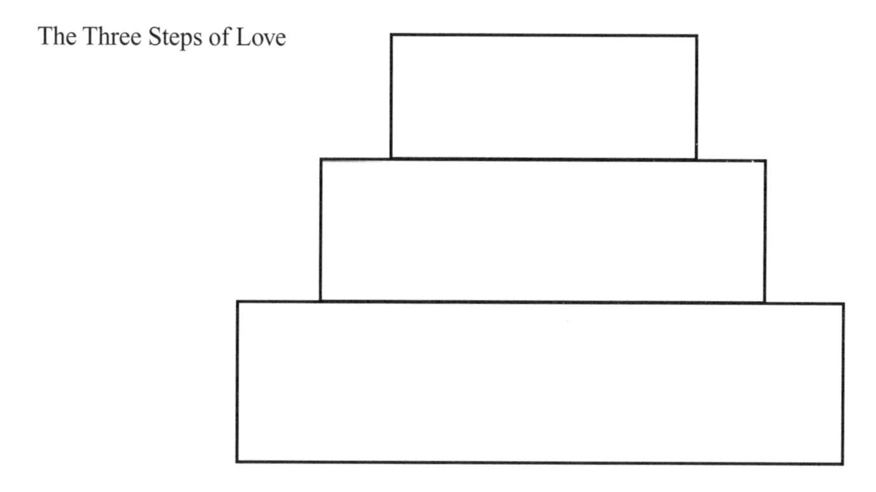

27. When you first read this passage, what stood out to you?

28. Now that you've examined the passage, what strikes you most?

29. Reflect on this story. How are you different from Jesus? How does he affect you? What do you think of him?

ME	JESUS

Gospel Connection:

This one incident reflects the pattern of Jesus' life: he looks at us, feels compassion, and acts by giving his life on the cross for us. That is the gospel. Sometimes Jesus' death on the cross seems abstract, but by connecting it with his life, we see how concrete God's love is for us. Through Jesus, God looks at us, feels our pain, and acts for us. We are not alone.

LESSON 1 APPLICATION

1. What did the Spirit help you see about either Jesus or yourself through this lesson?

2. How does Jesus affect you as he loves the widow of Nain? What inspires, convicts, or encourages you?

3. How do Jesus' words to the grieving woman, "Don't cry," challenge your assumptions about feelings?

4. Think about the three steps of love: looking, compassion, and helping. Which comes most naturally to you? Which do you typically ignore or underemphasize?

5. What would happen if you helped a person without looking at him or her or feeling compassion? What if you looked and felt compassion but did not help? Why are all three actions necessary?

6. How does Jesus demonstrate humility in this story? What makes that striking for you?

7. How does Jesus' posture of humility and love contrast with how other people approach helping?

8. What is the connection between humility and love?

9. Reflect on your own life and relationships. How can you grow in humility?

LESSON 2: LOOKING

OUTLINE:

1. The Problem . . . . 15 mins
2. The Exchange. . . . . 5 mins
3. How Looking Leads to Love . . . . 10 mins
4. Learning to Cherish. . . . . 10 mins
5. The Looking of Jesus in His Life . . . . 5 mins

LESSON 2: LOOKING

SECTION 1: The Problem[1] 15 mins

We watched Jesus' behavior with the widow of Nain in the last lesson; now let's look at his teaching about love through a parable. Parables are simple stories meant to change how the listener thinks. Like Jesus' behavior, they are often startling.

Luke 10:30-35—The Good Samaritan

> [30] Jesus said: "A man was going down from Jerusalem to Jericho, when he was attacked by robbers. They stripped him of his clothes, beat him and went away, leaving him half dead. [31] A priest happened to be going down the same road, and when he saw the man, he passed by on the other side. [32] So too, a Levite, when he came to the place and saw him, passed by on the other side. [33] But a Samaritan, as he traveled, came where the man was; and when he saw him, he took pity on him. [34] He went to him and bandaged his wounds, pouring on oil and wine. Then he put the man on his own donkey, brought him to an inn and took care of him. [35] The next day he took out two denarii and gave them to the innkeeper. 'Look after him,' he said, 'and when I return, I will reimburse you for any extra expense you may have.'

Historical Background: Geography

- When Jesus said, "A man was going down from Jerusalem to Jericho," his audience immediately smelled danger. It was like saying, "A man was walking by an inner-city bar one night."
- The 18-mile Jericho-Jerusalem road snaked through an uninhabitable desert. It was little more than a footpath clinging to the side of cliffs, providing hiding places for robbers.

---

[1] For a more in-depth look at the story of the Good Samaritan, see lessons 14-17 in Paul Miller's *Grace Through the Eyes of Jesus* (seeJesus Press, 2014).

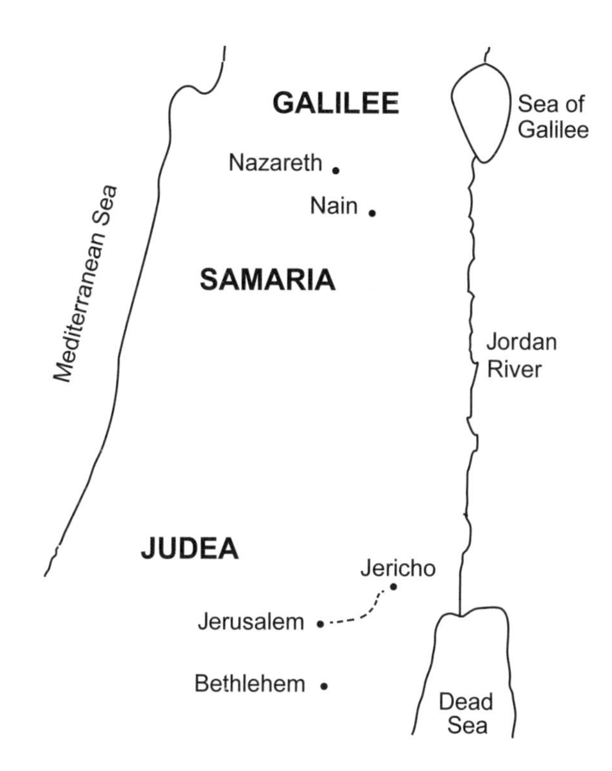

1. Today, if someone stops to help a stranded traveler, what do we call that person?

2. "Good Samaritan" sounds normal to us. What would you think if I said, "That person was a Good Terrorist"?

Historical Background: Priests, Levites, and Samaritans

- "Good Samaritan" sounded something like "Good Terrorist" to a first-century Jew. The Samaritans were a Jewish subculture that held sacred only the five books of Moses and worshipped in their own temple on Mount Gerizim instead of in Jerusalem.[2] Jews had no dealings with Samaritans. In fact, a Jewish person would not even eat from a bowl touched by a Samaritan.
- Look at the map above. The most direct route between the two major Jewish centers—Galilee to the north and Judea to the south—was through Samaria. But some Jews took the dangerous detour through the Jordan River valley to avoid setting foot in Samaria.

[2] There are some 400 Samaritans and a Samaritan High Priest alive today. See H.G.M. Williamson, "Samaritans," in *Dictionary of Jesus and the Gospels*. Eds. Joel B. Green and Scot McKnight. (Downers Grove, IL: InterVarsity Press, 1992), 724-728.

The priest and Levite weren't just any Jews. They were the religious elite:

- Priests were upper-class Levites descended from Aaron. Within the priesthood was a special group called the Sadducees, who were influenced by Greek culture. They controlled the temple through an even smaller subset, the Chief Priests. You can think of priests as "Religious Governors."
- Levites were middle-class farmers who came to the temple two weeks a year to preside over the offerings. Zechariah, John the Baptist's father, was a Levite. These are the "Religious Mayors."

3. When Jesus' audience hears a story about a priest and a Levite, who do they expect the third character to be?

4. What does Jesus communicate by having these temple officials walk past the injured man?

Historical Background: Tribalism

In the ancient world, each person belonged to a tribe from whom he or she derived a sense of identity and safety. People understood how to use markers, such as speech or clothing, to quickly identify the tribe of another person. We call that tribalism.

5. How do people in one tribe tend to relate to those outside their tribe?

6. What clues do we have about the beaten man's tribe?

7. Why does Jesus make it difficult for the people in the story to discover the victim's tribe?

8. **Why does Jesus choose a Samaritan to be the "good guy" and priests and Levites to be "bad guys"?**

SECTION 2: The Exchange 5 mins

9. **How is the Samaritan inconvenienced?**

10. **How is the Samaritan's response to the wounded man similar to Jesus' response to the widow of Nain?**

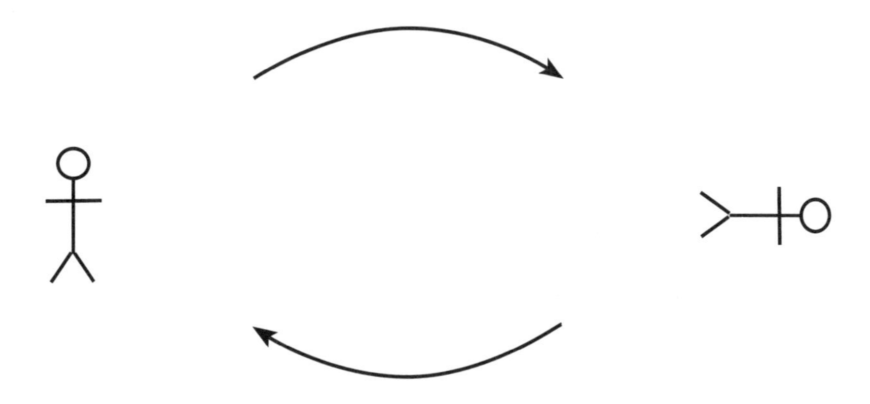

11. How does this diagram remind us of the gospel?

Gospel Connection:

Every act of love involves an exchange. This movement of love is the heart of the gospel, the good news: Jesus exchanges his life for ours. We will begin to see that these small incidents in Jesus' life suggest his greatest act of love. *(Do not feel you need to do more than hint at the gospel now.)*

SECTION 3: How Looking Leads to Love — 10 mins

12. Why do we look away when we see someone begging by the roadside?

13. What other situations tempt us to look away, as the priest and Levite did?

14. What do the priest and Levite see when they see this man? What does the Samaritan see?

15. Does God see you as a problem or a person? If you see yourself as a problem, how does this story help you?

16. How does this pattern—looking leading to compassion leading to helping—help us learn to love the people in our lives?

Insight: How Looking Helps Us to Love

- When confronting a difficult situation, we can get overwhelmed. Often we don't know how to begin. But we can begin by looking. We might not feel compassion, but we can concentrate on another person. By keeping him or her in front of us, we open the door to compassion.
- Often we become frozen when someone is upset about a problem with no apparent solution. We want to give him or her a quick word of advice and move on. The idea of "looking" helps us to relax. It is okay to look and listen without having a solution.
- Principle: Love begins with looking.

SECTION 4: Learning to Cherish — 10 mins

At the time I was studying how Jesus looked at people, I noticed how Jill "looked" at Kim when she was at school. Kim has poor muscle tone so she struggled in getting around school. This was especially true at one particular school because it had so many stairs in it. (Jill's fears were not groundless, by the way. Several years later Kim fell, broke her elbow, and had to have several operations.) Likewise, lunchtime was a hard time for Kim because she didn't have any friends, so she would often sit alone when she ate. Jill was completely powerless to help her during the school day, but she concentrated on her all day long. She knew when she was changing classes, so she would pray for her when she was going up and down the steps. She prayed for her during lunchtime when she was alone. She "looked" at her all day long. Jill's looking fed her compassion, which in turn led her to bear her burdens through prayer.[3]

Jesus' teaching on the eye helps to explain why looking leads to compassion.

Matthew 6:22

[22] The eye is the lamp of the body.

---

[3] Paul Miller, *Love Walked Among Us* (Colorado Springs: NavPress, 2001), 34.

Insight:
Looking—watching, observing—draws us into what we're looking at. We tend to look at things that give us life. So, if we focus on money all the time, we'll be drawn into the love of money.

17. If the eye is the lamp of the body, then what is Jesus' eye full of?

18. What do you think the priest and Levite were cherishing?

19. Have you ever had someone cherish you? What was it like?

Gospel Connection:
All of us long to be cherished, yet we are often slow to cherish others. We want someone else's mind to be full of us, for someone to care about how we are doing each moment of the day, but we seldom do that for others. The heart of the Gospels is that, in Jesus, God is cherishing us. He begins by looking at us. *(We will develop this point further in the next lesson.)*

SECTION 5: The Looking of Jesus in His Life — 5 mins

Skim the Scripture passages below. Don't focus on details, but watch for a pattern.

a. **Widow of Nain:**
   "And when the Lord saw her, he felt **compassion** for her…" (Luke 7:13).
b. **Traveling around teaching and healing:**
   "When he **saw** the crowds, he had **compassion** on them" (Matthew 9:36).

c. **Feeding of 5,000:**
   "Jesus looked up and **saw**..." (John 6:5).
   "When Jesus landed and saw a large crowd, he had **compassion** on them" (Matthew 14:14).
   "When Jesus landed and **saw** a large crowd, he had **compassion** on them, because they were like sheep without a shepherd. So he began teaching them many things" (Mark 6:34).
d. **Rich young ruler:**
   "Jesus **looked** at him and **loved** him..." (Mark 10:21).
e. **Zacchaeus:**
   "[Jesus] **looked** up and said to him, 'Zacchaeus, come down immediately. I must stay at your house today'" (Luke 19:5).
f. **After the death of Lazarus:**
   "When Jesus saw [Mary] weeping, and the Jews who came with her also weeping, he was deeply moved in spirit and troubled" (John 11:33).
g. **Seeing Jerusalem:**
   "As he approached Jerusalem and **saw** the city, he **wept** over it" (Luke 19:41).
h. **Mary at the cross:**
   "When Jesus **saw** his mother there, and the disciple whom he loved standing nearby, he said to his mother, 'Dear woman, here is your son,' and to the disciple, 'Here is your mother.'..." (John 19:26).

20. What patterns did you see?

LESSON 2 APPLICATION

1. What did the Spirit help you see about either Jesus or yourself through this lesson?

2. Read Luke 10:25-29, the verses immediately preceding this parable. To whom is Jesus teaching this story? Why might the parable be particularly disruptive to him? What assumptions is Jesus turning upside down?

3. How does Jesus capture your imagination in the detailed descriptions of people he paints in this story?

4. Take ten minutes this week and simply look at people, whether strangers in a public place or people you know at work or home. What thoughts come to your mind? What do you see now that you might normally miss?

5. When, in the last week, have you looked away—seeing someone as a problem or an interruption rather than an opportunity to love?

6. Think of a difficult relationship in your life. Write that person's initials here: ________. If you really look at him or her, what do you see? What will it cost you to move toward that person in love? How can you help?

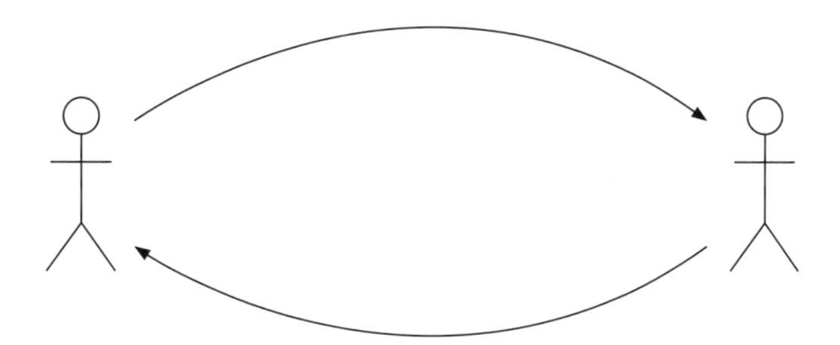

7. Jesus is the true Good Samaritan. He sees you and your needs, cherishes you, and comes to your aid. How have you experienced his burden-bearing love?

8. Pray with someone in your group that the Spirit will help you love like Jesus—joyfully looking, feeling, and helping even when it is costly.

9. Jesus is deliberately provocative when he makes the "good guy" a Samaritan. He is addressing cultural, political, and religious divides. What cultural and political divides do you feel uncomfortable bridging?

LESSON 2 ADDENDUM

Below is a list of Gospel passages that mention Jesus looking at people, telling people to look, or teaching about looking. Some merely refer to Jesus noticing, while others stress the activity of Jesus' looking.

(Note: "(2x)" refers to the number of distinct times that Jesus is mentioned as looking in the different texts— i.e., it is not two parallel accounts but two separate incidents of looking in one context.)

1. (2x) Matthew 19:26: "Jesus looked at them and said..." Mark 10:23,27: "Jesus looked around..."
2. Mark 3:5, Luke 6:10: "He looked around at them in anger..."
3. Matthew 9:22: "Jesus turned and saw her. 'Take heart, daughter'..." Mark 5:32: "But Jesus kept looking around…"
4. Luke 19:5: "When Jesus reached the spot, he looked up and said to him, 'Zacchaeus, come down...'."
5. Luke 20:17: "Jesus looked directly at them and asked, 'Then what is the meaning...'."
6. (2x) Luke 21:1: "As he looked up, Jesus saw the rich putting their gifts into the temple treasury." Luke 21:2: "He also saw a poor widow put in two very small copper coins."
7. Luke 22:61: "The Lord turned and looked straight at Peter."
8. (2x) John 1:47: "When Jesus saw Nathanael approaching, he said of him..." John 1:48: "Jesus answered, 'I saw you under the fig tree before Philip called you.'"
9. Matthew 3:7: "But when he saw many of the Pharisees and Sadducees coming..."
10. Matthew 4:18: "As Jesus walked by the Sea of Galilee, he saw two brothers..."
11. (2x) Matthew 4:21, Mark 1:19: "Going on from there, he saw two other brothers..."
12. Mark 1:16: "As Jesus walked beside the Sea of Galilee, he saw Simon and his brother Andrew..."
13. Matthew 5:1: "Now when he saw the crowds, he went up on a mountainside and sat down."
14. Matthew 8:14: "When Jesus came into Peter's house, he saw Peter's mother-in-law lying in bed..."
15. Matthew 8:18: "When Jesus saw the crowd around him, he gave orders to cross to the other side..."
16. Matthew 9:2, Mark 2:5: "When Jesus saw their faith, he said to the paralytic, 'Take heart, son...'." Luke 5:20: "When he saw their faith, he said, 'Friend, your sins are forgiven.'"
17. Matthew 9:9: "As Jesus went on from there, he saw a man called Matthew sitting at a tax collector's booth." Mark 2:14, Luke 5:27: "As he walked along, he saw Levi son of Alphaeus..."
18. Matthew 9:23: "When Jesus entered the ruler's house and saw the flute players and the noisy crowd…" Mark 5:38: "...Jesus saw a commotion, with people crying and wailing loudly."
19. Matthew 9:36: "When he saw the crowds, he had compassion on them..."
20. Matthew 14:14, Mark 6:34: "When Jesus landed and saw a large crowd, he had compassion on them..." John 6:5: "When Jesus looked up and saw a large crowd coming toward him, he asked Philip..."
21. Mark 8:33: "But when Jesus turned and looked at his disciples, he rebuked Peter…"
22. Mark 6:48: "He saw the disciples straining at the oars, because the wind was against them…"
23. Mark 9:25: "When Jesus saw that a crowd was running to the scene, he rebuked the evil spirit…"

24. Mark 10:14: "When Jesus saw this, he was indignant. He said to them, 'Let the little children come.'"
25. Luke 7:13: "When the Lord saw her, his heart went out to her and he said, 'Don't cry.'"
26. Luke 13:12: "When Jesus saw her, he called her forward and said to her, 'Woman, you are set free.'"
27. Luke 17:14: "When he saw them, he said, 'Go, show yourselves to the priests.'"
28. Luke 19:41: "As he approached Jerusalem and saw the city, he wept over it."
29. John 1:38: "Turning around, Jesus saw them following and asked, 'What do you want?'"
30. John 5:6: "When Jesus saw him lying there and learned that he had been in this condition…"
31. John 9:1: "As he went along, he saw a man blind from birth."
32. John 11:33: "When Jesus saw her weeping, and the Jews who had come along with her also weeping…"
33. John 19:26: "When Jesus saw his mother there, and the disciple whom he loved standing nearby…"
34. Luke 7:44: "Then he turned toward the woman and said to Simon, 'Do you see this woman?"

LESSON 3: THE FATHER'S LOOKING

OUTLINE:

1. Looking . . . . 5 mins
2. The Father's Looking . . . . 10 mins
3. The Father's Shame . . . . 15 mins
4. Jesus' Looking = God's Looking at Us . . . . 15 mins

LESSON 3: THE FATHER'S LOOKING

SECTION 1: Looking 5 mins

1. **What does it mean to look at someone? Or what is the opposite of looking? You can give answers on either side of the chart.**

LOOKING	NOT LOOKING

SECTION 2: The Father's Looking 10 mins

Insight:

The Pharisees essentially criticize Jesus for hanging out at the local bar with lowlifes (Luke 15:1-2; Matthew 11:19). In response, Jesus tells them three stories. We'll read part of the third story now.

Luke 15:11-24—The Lost Son

[11] Jesus continued: "There was a man who had two sons. [12] The younger one said to his father, 'Father, give me my share of the estate.' So he divided his property between them.

[13] "Not long after that, the younger son got together all he had, set off for a distant country and there squandered his wealth in wild living.[14] After he had spent everything, there was a severe famine in that whole country, and he began to be in need. [15] So he went and hired himself out to a citizen of that country, who sent him to his fields to feed pigs. [16] He longed to fill his stomach with the pods that the pigs were eating, but no one gave him anything.

[17] "When he came to his senses, he said, 'How many of my father's hired servants have food to spare, and here I am starving to death! [18] I will set out and go back to my father and say to him: Father, I have sinned against heaven and against you. [19] I am no longer worthy to be called your son; make me like one of your hired servants.' [20] So he got up and went to his father.

"But while he was still a long way off, his father saw him and was filled with compassion for him; he ran to his son, threw his arms around him and kissed him.

[21] "The son said to him, 'Father, I have sinned against heaven and against you. I am no longer worthy to be called your son.'

[22] "But the father said to his servants, 'Quick! Bring the best robe and put it on him. Put a ring on his finger and sandals on his feet. [23] Bring the fattened calf and kill it. Let's have a feast and celebrate. [24] For this son of mine was dead and is alive again; he was lost and is found.' So they began to celebrate."

2. What does the father in this story do that is similar to what we saw in the stories of the Good Samaritan and widow of Nain?

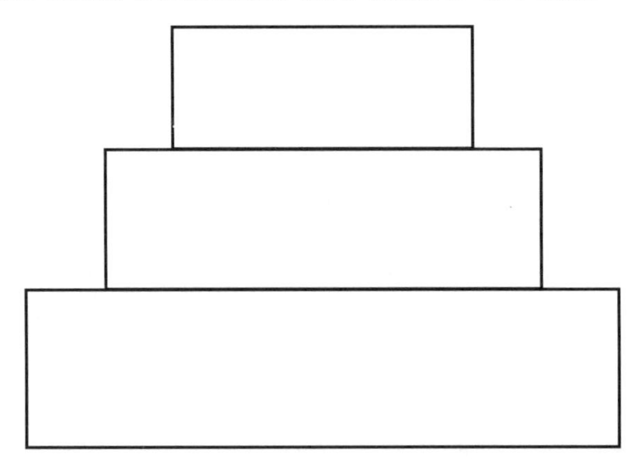

Historical Background: "Compassion" in Greek

All three stories (Widow of Nain, Good Samaritan, Lost Son) use the same Greek word to describe compassion. The Greek word is more emphatic than our English word; it means you feel something in your gut.[1] The NIV is trying to capture the strength of this Greek word through the phrase "his heart went out to her."

3. How is the father's response to his son different from Jesus' response to the widow of Nain or the Samaritan's response to the beaten man?

4. The Middle East has a treeless horizon, so you can see someone a half-mile away. Where is the son when the father sees him?

5. What does that tell you about the father's looking?

SECTION 3: The Father's Shame — 15 mins

6. Why does the father run to his son?

Insight:

Now let's picture this from the villagers' perspective. Imagine you live in a small town with one factory. The factory owner's son pressures his father into selling the factory to a large firm which closes the factory and leaves you and your family unemployed. Then the son spends all the money from the factory at the casino before returning to town to hunt for a job.

---

[1] Warfield, "The Emotional Life of our Lord," 96.

Insight:

Let's imagine another scenario. Your father leaves home when you are five years old. You watch your mother struggle through college while maintaining a household without alimony or child support. When you are a teenager, your absentee father shows up, apologizes to your mom, and asks for a loan.

Historical Background: Village Participation

An angry reception would have been inevitable for the son in the ancient Near East. In fact, the young boys of the village would likely greet him at the edge of town. They would spread the word, so the whole village could gather to throw stones at him.

7. Given this context, why else might the father run to his son?

Historical Background: Ancient Near Eastern Patriarchs

Patriarchs in the ancient Near East don't run, even to this day. Scholar Kenneth Bailey recalls a time when a pastor in the Middle East was rejected by a church because he walked too fast.[2] A cultural equivalent might be a dignified older man showing up for a sales call at a Fortune 500 company in jogging shorts. But the father has no choice. If he wants to beat the mob, he has to run. He has to shame himself to rescue his son.

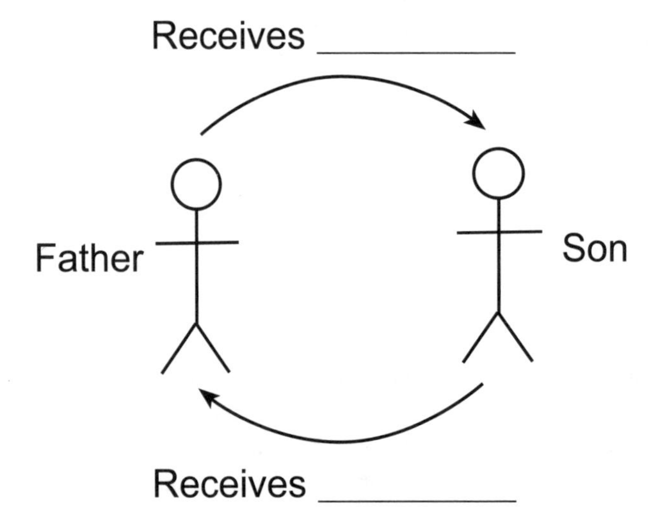

[2] Kenneth Bailey, *Through Peasant Eyes* (Grand Rapids, MI: Eerdmans, 1996), 181.

8. Initially, do the father and the son physically exchange anything when they embrace?

9. What does the son gain?

10. What does the father gain?

Gospel Connection:

- Every act of love involves an exchange.
- Remember how the Samaritan substitutes his money for the sickness of the man on the roadside? Love always comes with a cost.
- The same thing happens on the cross. Our sin and self-centeredness go on Jesus, and we receive his love and righteousness. Second Corinthians 5:21 says, "God made him who had no sin to be sin for us, so that in him we might become the righteousness of God."
- What does this have to do with love? It means God is giving us the power to love by loving us. You cannot love unless you are loved. The only one who can do that completely is God.

SECTION 4: Jesus' Looking = God's Looking at Us 15 mins

Exodus 3:7

God said, "I have indeed seen the misery of my people in Egypt…and I am concerned about their suffering."

11. What two things do you see God doing here? Where else have you seen this pattern?

Theological Background: Jesus Behaving Like God

- Luke, a careful student of the Scriptures, would have been aware that Jesus' pattern of looking leading to compassion reflected the pattern of God's interaction with his people throughout the Old Testament.[3]

[3] Luke quotes Stephen in Acts 7:34, referring to God's pattern of relating as described in Exodus 3:7. Looking is a distinctive characteristic of God's relating in the Old Testament. When God looks he acts, so many psalms are prayers for God to look on the psalmist's condition.

- By noticing and drawing attention to this pattern in Jesus, Luke suggests what Gospel authors frequently suggest: when we watch Jesus, we're watching God love us. Like the father in the parable, God's eyes are glued to the horizon. When he sees us, he lifts up his garment and shamelessly gallops toward us and our load of guilt and despair. He wraps us in his arms and smothers us with kisses.
- This is not new behavior for God. He has looked at people with compassion for centuries. Jesus' eyes give God a face.

Insight: Vision of Sadhu Sadar Singh[4]

Corrie ten Boom, the author of the story I'm about to read, was imprisoned by the Nazis during WWII, along with her sister and father, for hiding Jews in their home in Holland. Her father and sister died there, but Corrie lived to share her story. *This story illustrates the power and beauty of Jesus' eyes and how we experience his compassion through them. Feel free to use your own illustration instead.*

The Story of the Sadhu

A person who influenced my life in my late teens was a man from India. As a boy he had come to hate Jesus. He knew about God, but the Bible of the Christians was a book which he believed was a gigantic lie. Once he took a Bible and burned it, feeling that with this act, he could publicly declare his scorn of what he believed were the untruths it contained. When missionaries passed him he threw mud on them.

But there was a terrible unrest inside of him; he longed to know God. He told this story about himself: "Although I had believed that I had done a very good deed by burning the Bible, I felt unhappy. After three days, I couldn't bear it any longer. I rose early in the morning and prayed that if God really existed, He would reveal himself to me. I wanted to know if there was an existence after death, if there was a heaven. The only way I could know it for sure was to die. So I decided to die.

"I planned to throw myself in front of the train which passed by our house. Then suddenly something unusual happened. The room was filled with a beautiful glow and I saw a man. I thought it might be Buddha, or some other holy man. Then I heard a voice.

"'How long will you deny Me? I died for you; I have given my life for you.'

"Then I saw his hands—the pierced hands of Jesus Christ. This was the Christ I had imagined as a great man who once lived in Palestine, but who died and disappeared. And yet now stood before me... alive! I saw his face looking at me with love.

---

4 Regarding visions: Some people undermine the authority of biblical revelation by exalting visions, deriving doctrine from them or making visions their goal. Paul warns the Colossians (2:18) about the person who "takes his stand" on visions. Nevertheless, Scripture repeatedly references visions and God speaking in visions or dreams. We hear about the Lord using dreams today in the lives of Hindus and Muslims on the edge of conversion. In Sadar's vision, I was struck by how the reference to Jesus' eyes is similar to the pattern in the Gospels. I assume neither the Sadar nor Corrie knew of this pattern. Ravi Zacharias notes that Islam as a religion is filled with references to visions and angels. He suggests that God uses the forms of a particular culture when he speaks to it. Lee Strobel, *The Case for Faith* (Grand Rapids, MI: Zondervan, 2000), 162. [If you have reservations about the vision story, don't use it.]

“Three days before, I had burned the Bible, and yet he was not angry. I was suddenly changed...I saw him as Christ, the living One, the Savior of the world. I fell on my knees and knew a wonderful peace, which I had never found anywhere before. That was the happiness I had been seeking for such a long time.”

That weekend as I listened to the Sadhu, I was amazed but disturbed. He told of the visions he had seen—of how he really saw Jesus—at a time when he didn’t believe. We had all read about the Apostle Paul’s experiences on the road to Damascus, but here was a man who claimed to have had this experience himself.

One boy ventured to ask the question we all wanted to know. “Please, sir, how did Jesus look?”

He put his hands before his eyes and said, “Oh, his eyes, his eyes...they are so beautiful.” Since then I have longed to see Jesus’ eyes.[5]

12. How does studying Jesus’ eyes and his looking in this passage impact you? What do you think about him?

[5] Corrie ten Boom with Carole C. Carlson, *In My Father’s House* (Old Tappan, NJ: Fleming Revell, 1976), 82-84.

LESSON 3 APPLICATION

1. What did the Spirit help you see about either Jesus or yourself through this lesson?

2. Put yourself in the lost son's shoes and recount your journey home. What emotions did you experience? What did you risk? How did it feel to see your father galloping toward you?

3. Have you ever "[come] to your senses" as the lost son did? As you are comfortable, share what happened and how God rescued you.

4. Jesus could have told this parable without highlighting the father's compassion; it would be a powerful story if the father and son merely exchanged a handshake. Why did Jesus add these seemingly unnecessary details?

5. How have you experienced this kind of welcome from God? Describe what happened.

6. In what ways does the father in this story resemble our heavenly Father?

7. How does God's love give you power to love others?

8. What impacts you most about the story of the Sadhu?

LESSON 4: JUDGING

OUTLINE:

1. Judging and Looking . . . . 15 mins
2. Reflecting on Judging and Compassion . . . . 15 mins
3. Comparing Two Paths . . . . 10 mins
4. Gospel Connection . . . . 5 mins

LESSON 4: JUDGING

SECTION 1: Judging and Looking 15 mins

John 9:1-7—A Man Born Blind

[1] As he went along, he saw a man blind from birth. [2] His disciples asked him, "Rabbi, who sinned, this man or his parents, that he was born blind?"

[3] "Neither this man nor his parents sinned," said Jesus, "but this happened so that the works of God might be displayed in him. [4] As long as it is day, we must do the works of him who sent me. Night is coming, when no one can work. [5] While I am in the world, I am the light of the world."

[6] After saying this, he spit on the ground, made some mud with the saliva, and put it on the man's eyes. [7] "Go," he told him, "wash in the Pool of Siloam" (this word means "Sent"). So the man went and washed, and came home seeing.

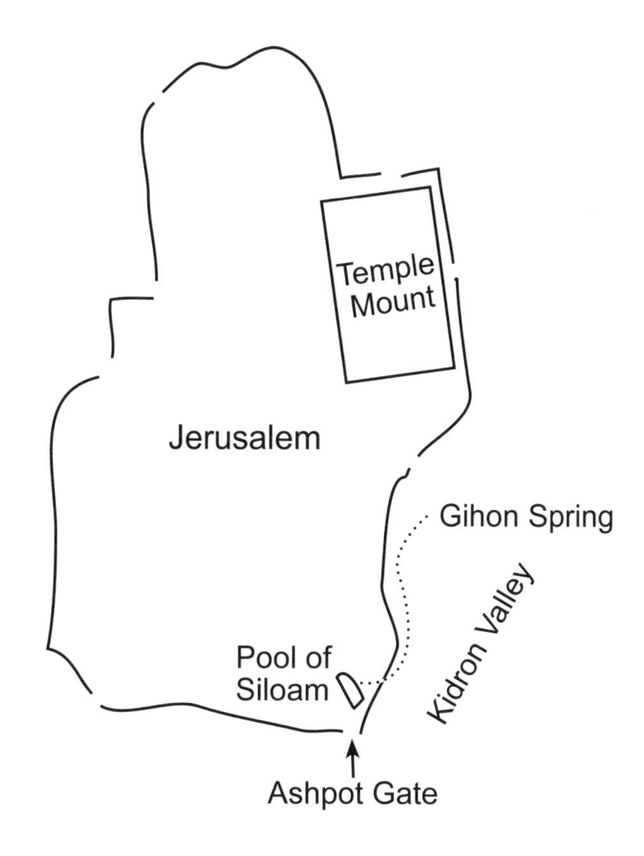

Historical Background: Pool of Siloam

- In the first century, you had to beg by the roadside if a disability prevented you from working. City gates were the best place to beg because people were forced to look at you. Jesus and his disciples were likely walking by a city gate, like the Ashpot Gate next to the Pool of Siloam, where this exchange took place.
- Siloam means "sent" in Hebrew. The water in the pool is "sent" from the Gihon Spring in the Kidron Valley. King Hezekiah dug the channel before the Assyrian attack in 701 B.C. to provide a water source for Jerusalem (2 Chronicles 32:30). It is nearly 1,800 feet long and cut through solid bedrock. Water flows through it to this day.[1]

1. How does Jesus relate to the blind man, and how do the disciples relate to him?

JESUS	DISCIPLES

2. Why do you think Jesus initially looks but says nothing?

3. What effect does Jesus just looking have on the disciples?

[1] D.A. Carson, *The Gospel According to John* (Grand Rapids, MI: InterVarsity Press, 1991), 365.

SECTION 2: Reflecting on Judging and Compassion 15 mins

4. When the disciples finally notice the blind man, what do they do to him—in a word?

5. If you were the blind man and you overheard the disciples' question, how would you feel?

6. How would you feel if you overheard what Jesus said about you?

Historical Background: Kindness, Then and Now

In Jesus' day, people did not value compassion and kindness. It was a time when Alexander the Great was hero and few cared for the poor. There was no Mother Teresa, Red Cross, or Red Crescent; compassion was muted and limited. Jesus made compassion a public value.

7. What's the difference between judging and showing compassion?

JUDGING	COMPASSION

Illustration: Reflections of a husband and wife on how they judge one another

A wife's reflections:

"I judge him when he is tired. I make him feel he has no right expressing his fatigue when I want him to do otherwise. I judge him when he is not helping me keep the house straight. I judge his pain tolerance. (This one is interesting. I did always question the intensity of the pains he would complain about, assuming it was not as bad as he was making it out to be. But sure enough, in the last few months God has given me two exact ailments that my husband has had and expressed his pain over. Of course, I told him over and over again how badly he has been hurting. Boy, I have been cruel and insensitive to not show compassion to him when he expresses pain.)

"...I have a hard time not explaining my side as I write some of the above. This leads me to believe I judge my husband even as he shares the way I hurt him, judge him, dishonor him, etc., instead of listening and learning about how my sins hurt him and how I could love him better.

"He says that my 'rules' make him sad and lonely. That makes me sad. He stated, ever so wisely, that the reason I don't see my laws is because I am so caught in the image of myself as the little girl trying to please her parents by doing everything correctly and efficiently."

A husband's reflections:

"My attitude is something like, 'Don't tell me what's right—I already know. I even try to know my sin before anyone else does. With the family my rule is, 'Don't challenge my authority.' It is also important to me that people be competent—I judge people who consistently struggle. They wear me out.

"My wife says that I judge her about things she likes to do that I don't have a natural affinity to. She feels judged about what she wants done to the house, i.e., 'you are being worldly.' I judge her about the novels she likes reading and make her feel that she should be reading spiritual material.

"...My rules make my wife feel like getting away from me and rebelling against me. She feels resentment and a slow simmering anger. She senses my high commitment to being right as part of my blindness. She notes that this is especially bad when there is someone I respect that I am trying to please with my obedience. My concern over gaining respect is more important than loving her. I want to be rid of this judging heart."

8. Having listened to these reflections, can you now think of specific ways you judge your spouse, coworker, or friend?

9. Why do we judge? What does it do for us?

Insight:

We tend to recognize judging as a problem only when our judgments are inaccurate. For example, we thought someone lied when we really misunderstood them. But there are at least two ways our judgments can be accurate and yet still wrong:

1. My insight is correct, but I have a judgmental spirit. I feel superior to the other person.
2. My insight is correct, but I overstate the negative in the other person's life and miss all the good.

In either case, I assume a god-like stance above the other person with my judgmental spirit. I put myself on the throne and judge others from that superior position.

In Unit Two of this study, we will learn the difference between a judgmental spirit and good honesty. Speaking the truth in love—good honesty—is one of the best gifts we give others. But good honesty doesn't speak from above—that's judgment.

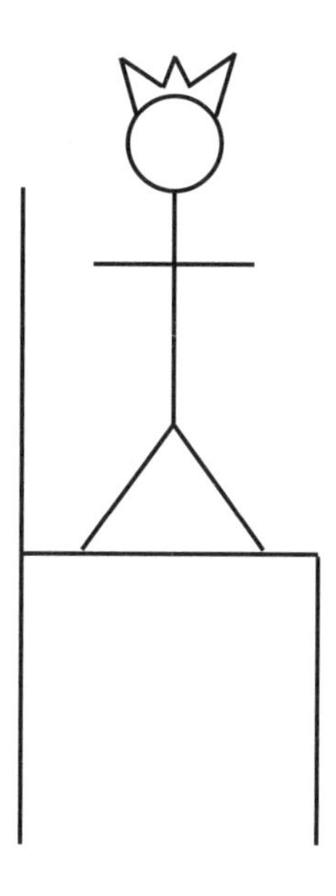

Insight:

Henri Nouwen left Harvard Divinity School to live in a community devoted to the care of disabled adults. He reflects:

"To die to our neighbors means to stop judging them, to stop evaluating them, and thus to become free to be compassionate. Compassion can never co-exist with judgment because judgment creates the distance, the distinction, which prevents us from really being with the other…'Do not judge and you will not be judged yourselves' [Matthew 7:1] is a word of Jesus that is indeed very hard to live up to. But it contains the secret of compassion."[2]

---

2 Henri J. M. Nouwen, *The Way of the Heart: The Spirituality of the Desert Fathers and Mothers* (San Francisco: Harper, 1991), 35.

Modern Culture: Judging

It is no longer fashionable to talk about sin, but that doesn't stop us from judging. Our "knowledge" of psychology has increased our ability to label one another more accurately. "She has 'daddy issues,'" or "He's a little obsessive," we say. We get a small insight into people and judge them accordingly.

SECTION 3: Comparing Two Paths — 10 mins

10. What is Jesus' three-step path of compassion?

11. Why is it helpful to see this as a path?

12. There are multiple paths of judging. What might a three-step path of judging look like?

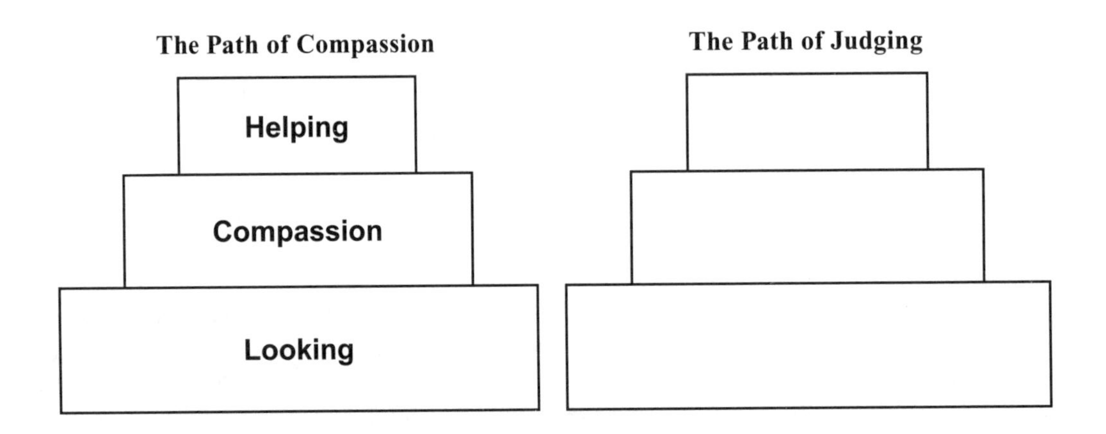

13. What happens to a relationship if you take the compassion path? The judging path?

Insight:

The following chart shows the contrast between the paths of judging and compassion.

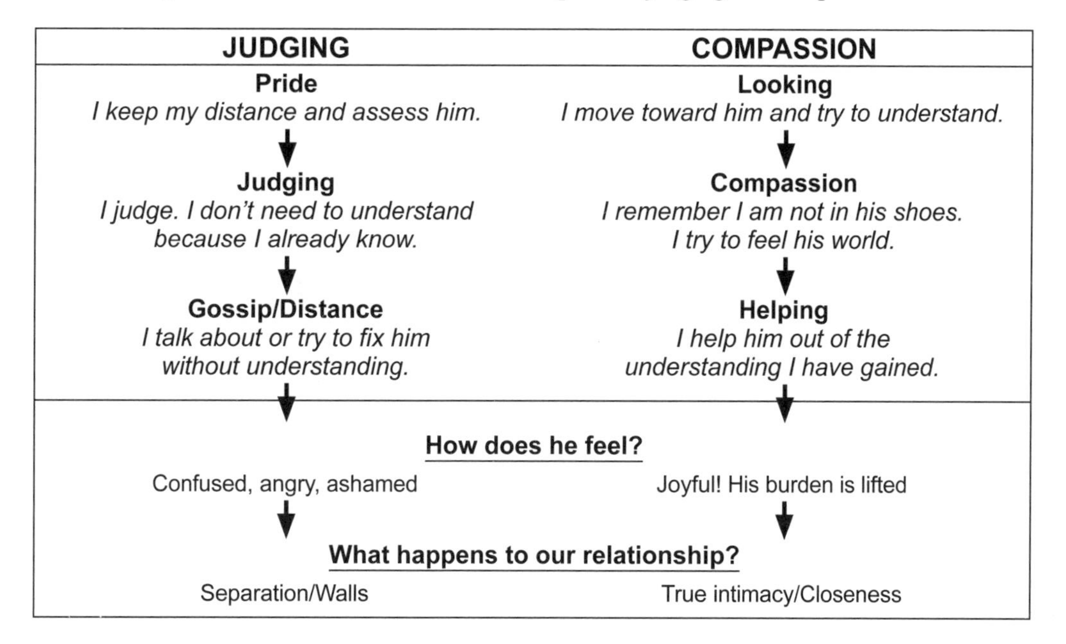

SECTION 4: Gospel Connection 5 mins

Insight:

This seemingly small encounter with the blind man is part of a larger pattern in Jesus' life. Listen to Jesus describe his role in John 3:17: "For God did not send his Son into the world to condemn the world, but to save the world through him."

What that means:

"God didn't go to all the trouble of sending his Son merely to point an accusing finger, telling the world how bad it was. He came to help, to put the world right again" (*The Message*).

"I haven't come to tell you what to do, but to move toward you to take your burden. I don't stand outside you and criticize; I come inside to comfort you" (AT).

Insight:

God looked at us, saw our condition, and met our deepest need—salvation—in Jesus. His death on the cross was a saving act instead of a judging act. Humanity deserved the wrath of God for its rebellion. But instead of judging the human race, God saved it by judging his son. Second Corinthians 5:21: "God made him who had no sin to be sin for us, so that in him we might become the righteousness of God."

LESSON 4 APPLICATION

1. What did the Spirit help you see about either Jesus or yourself through this lesson?

"My Day of Judgment" by Mike Yaconelli

I have a difficult time with judgmental people. They are so … judgmental. They have a gift for making you feel like something is wrong with you. There is an arrogance about them, an I-can't-believe-you-call-yourself-a-Christian attitude that seeks you out in a crowded room and lets you know you are not OK.

These people are worse than politically correct, they have God on their side… They are always right. Never wrong.

They have no problems.

They know what's wrong with this world…and with me.

And they are not the least bit timid in letting the world know just how those wrongs should be righted.

Memories? Boy, do they have them. Make a mistake or, worse yet, sin so that they find out about it, and you are doomed. They will not let you or anyone else forget. Ever. They want to keep you in your place, make sure you don't get away with anything…I don't like people like that. Judgmental people have done so much damage in the name of God. They have hurt so many people, caused so much pain....

Let me give you an example of what I am talking about. A few weeks ago, my wife and I were having some remodeling done to our house. The contractor called to say that one of the subcontractors was coming over to do some work. He mentioned the man's name and I immediately balked. I told the contractor that we would rather not have this person come to our house because we knew some things about him that made it difficult for us to be around him. He had a drinking problem, and his son had been to see my wife and me two years previously and had some serious emotional scars that had been inflicted by this man. We had talked many hours with the son and the mother and tried to help them through a difficult time. Even though the man had left town for two years and had supposedly been to rehab, we were not happy to have an alcoholic, wife-abuser over to work on our home.

However, when the contractor pointed out that our remodeling job would be delayed, we decided to let the subcontractor do the work. The job would only take three days and his bid of $350 was much lower than anyone else's. On the day he finished the job, I mentioned to him that if he stopped by my office I would give him a check for his portion of the work. He looked at me and said, "Oh, I was just going to talk to you about that. We need to talk about my bill." I immediately felt my face turn red, and I thought, "That [jerk]! He hasn't changed one bit. I knew I should never have given in, and now he is going to try and screw me out of more money." I was furious. "People never really change," I thought to myself.

He showed up at my office about 5:00. I was ready for him. He sat down and we exchanged small talk for a few minutes. He took out his book and began to write down the details of his bill. In the middle of writing on the invoice he looked up to me and stopped writing. Awkwardly, he began to speak, "Mike, a couple of years ago I was really a mess. My son and my wife experienced a lot of pain because of me and my drinking. I know that during that time both my wife and son came to you for counseling. You helped them through a really tough time in our lives. I have my son and my wife back again, thanks to you. I couldn't thank you then, but I'm thanking you now." He placed the invoice on my desk with the words written "paid in full," slowly stood, and shook my hand. Our eyes met. His were filled with tears of gratitude, mine were filled with tears of embarrassment, humiliation, and remorse. I sat at my desk for a long time. The silence was pointing its finger in my direction. I had just come face to face with the most judgmental person I have ever known...myself.

No wonder I have such a difficult time with judgmental people. I am one of them. No wonder I criticize judgmental people so loudly. If I scream loud enough maybe no one will hear the judgment dripping from my own voice.

I had judged this man.

I had written him off.

I had not forgiven him.

I had not forgotten his past, and I made sure everyone else was aware of it.

I had decided I was better than he was.

Judge not, that ye not be judged? Not only was I judged, I was judged by the person I was judging.

I owe that man an apology. I owe Jesus an apology...For how many years have I raged about the arrogance and judgmentalism of others? Maybe I need to get out of the judging business and into the loving business.

This man has no idea what he did for me. Maybe someday I'll get up enough courage to tell him.[3]

2. Why does Mike struggle so much with judgmental people? How does his confession affect you?

3. Have you ever been in a similar situation? Describe it.

4. Reflect on a time when someone judged you. What did it feel like? How did you respond? What happened to the relationship?

[3] The Wittenberg Door (May/June 1992).

5. In what areas are you quick to judge others? Where do you tend to show compassion?

6. Are there people whom you unconsciously treat like objects? Consider the following story as you respond:

   We have a friend who uses a wheelchair due to the weakening effects of Muscular Dystrophy. One day he was at a restaurant with a group of friends. When it was his turn to order, the server turned to his friends and said, "What does he want?" Her thinking was simple: "People in wheelchairs are not normal. You can't talk to odd people. So I'll talk to his friends." He had ceased to be a person and became a mere object, an extension of his wheelchair. The server put our friend—an electrical engineer—into a category, instead of seeing him as a person.[4]

7. To whom is God calling you to show compassion instead of judgment? Plot out a concrete three-step path (i.e., don't write "helping," write "review fractions again with Ginny and try to make it fun") on the blank chart below.

[4] Paul Miller, *Love Walked Among Us* (Colorado Springs, CO: NavPress, 2001), 39.

LESSON 5: TWO STORIES OF LIFE

OUTLINE:

1. Story #1: Sowing and Reaping . . . . 5 mins
2. Story #2: The Gospel . . . . 10 mins
3. Getting the Story Wrong . . . . 10 mins
4. "Light of the World" . . . . 10 mins
5. The Disciples Learn to Love . . . . 10 mins

LESSON 5: TWO STORIES OF LIFE

SECTION 1: Story #1: Sowing and Reaping 5 mins

1. **Recall last week's lesson from John 9. What do the disciples think caused the man's blindness when they ask, "Rabbi, who sinned, this man or his parents, that he was born blind?"**

2. **How would the disciples fill in this blank?**

   ______?______ → **Suffering**

3. **What does Jesus' statement suggest about the relationship between the man's behavior and his suffering?**

4. **How does this explain the disciples' assumption about the blind man?**

Insight: Sowing and Reaping

"A man reaps what he sows" (Galatians 6:7b) is a basic life principle. If you do bad things, then bad things will happen to you.

5. Is this principle of sowing and reaping true? Can anyone give an example?

6. Back to John 9: Since the man was born blind, what puzzles the disciples?

SECTION 2: Story #2—The Gospel 10 mins

7. So how does Jesus answer their either-or question? What new principle does he introduce?

8. How does Jesus' principle reframe the man's suffering?

9. What new storyline is Jesus introducing?

10. Why might Jesus be particularly familiar with this storyline? Where do we see it in his life?

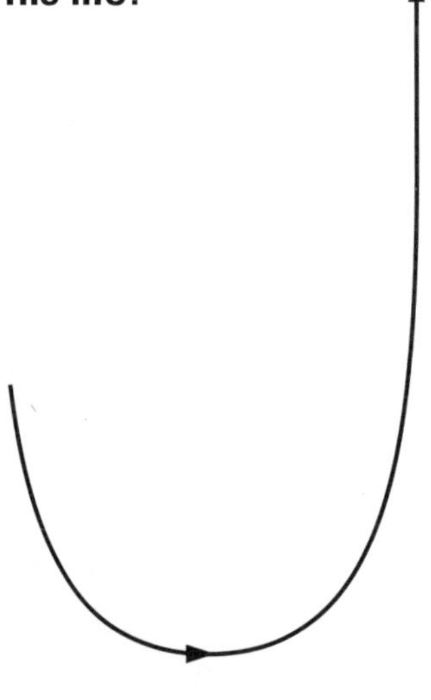

11. How does the *J-Curve* storyline liberate the blind man?

Historical Background: First Century vs. Modern Views of Suffering

In the first century, people saw suffering and asked what the person had done to offend God—so the sufferer directed his anger toward himself. In the 21st century, convinced of our basic innocence, we respond by being offended at and getting angry with God. Neither view considers the *J-Curve*.

12. So what mistake were the disciples initially making when they judged the blind man?

Gospel Connection: Law and Gospel

Sowing and reaping—Story #1—reflects the law; the *J-Curve*—Story #2—reflects the gospel. Both storylines are true. But if you have only the law storyline, you put people in "boxes." You define them by their sin, by how they hurt you. In short, you judge them. When taken together, the two storylines help you understand and value people.

Historical Background: Rigid Labels

In the Greek or pagan worldview, people were static—locked into fixed descriptions. Your label defined you. So this man's label—the blind man—was his whole identity. But a biblical worldview makes room for God's grace which transforms people. That's why the Bible doesn't force people into rigid roles like "angry Moses" or "wily Jacob." Biblical characters are dynamic—each is a "center of surprise" with the capacity to change and grow.[1]

SECTION 3: Getting the Story Wrong — 10 mins

John 9:13-17, 24-34

[13] They brought to the Pharisees the man who had been blind. [14] Now the day on which Jesus had made the mud and opened the man's eyes was a Sabbath. [15] Therefore the Pharisees also asked him how he had received his sight. "He put mud on my eyes," the man replied, "and I washed, and now I see."

---

[1] Robert Alter, *The Art of the Biblical Narrative* (New York: Basic Books, 2011), 158.

[16] Some of the Pharisees said, "This man is not from God, for he does not keep the Sabbath." But others asked, "How can a sinner perform such signs?" So they were divided.

[17] Then they turned again to the blind man, "What have you to say about him? It was your eyes he opened."

---

[24] A second time they summoned the man who had been blind. "Give glory to God by telling the truth," they said. "We know this man is a sinner."

[25] He replied, "Whether he is a sinner or not, I don't know. One thing I do know. I was blind but now I see!"

[26] Then they asked him, "What did he do to you? How did he open your eyes?"

[27] He answered, "I have told you already and you did not listen. Why do you want to hear it again? Do you want to become his disciples too?"

[28] Then they hurled insults at him and said, "You are this fellow's disciple! We are disciples of Moses! [29] We know that God spoke to Moses, but as for this fellow, we don't even know where he comes from."

[30] The man answered, "Now that is remarkable! You don't know where he comes from, yet he opened my eyes. [31] We know that God does not listen to sinners. He listens to the godly person who does his will. [32] Nobody has ever heard of opening the eyes of a man born blind. [33] If this man were not from God, he could do nothing."

[34] To this they replied, "You were steeped in sin at birth; how dare you lecture us!" And they threw him out.

13. Recall the disciples' question, "Who sinned, this man or his parents?" What is the Pharisees' answer to that question?

14. Based on their treatment of him, what do the Pharisees think about the blind man?

15. What is the blind man really like?

Insight:

Knowing the Pharisees despise Jesus, the formerly blind man asks them—with a show of innocence—if they want to hear his story because they secretly desire to become disciples themselves! His ironic, taunting question strips away all pretense of an even-handed evaluation. He is not only perceptive and bold, but he also has a sense of humor! Without a gospel storyline, the Pharisees cannot see him as a person.

16. So which story are the Pharisees applying to the situation? #1 or #2?

SECTION 4: "Light of the World" 10 mins

17. How have the Pharisees put Jesus in a box?

18. But what does Jesus say about himself?

Verses 3-5

[3] "Neither this man nor his parents sinned," said Jesus, "but this happened so that the works of God might be displayed in him. [4] As long as it is day, we must do the works of him who sent me. Night is coming, when no one can work. [5] While I am in the world, I am the light of the world."

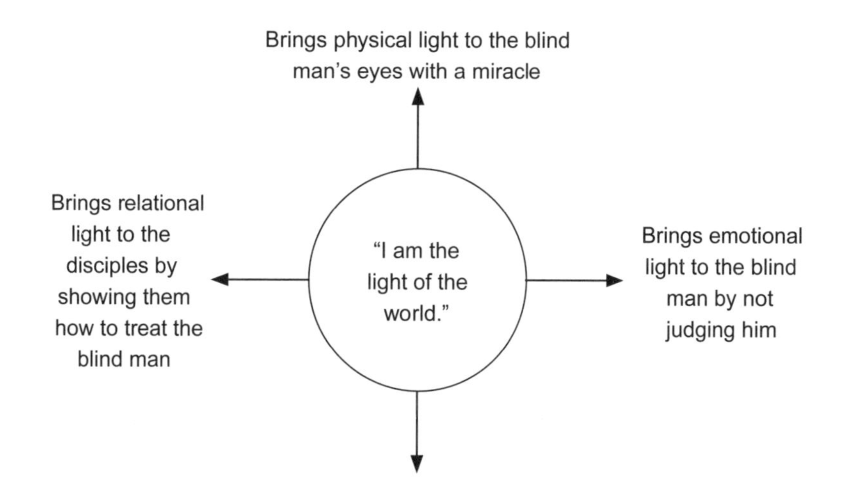

19. How is Jesus a light for the disciples in the story? The blind man?

Insight:

"Light of the world" makes sense when you see how Jesus lights up the lives of the people in this story. It also makes sense when you see that *what Jesus claims* ("I am the light of the world") is as extraordinary as *what he does* and *how he loves*. Jesus' claim would seem ludicrous if not for his extraordinary love and power.

20. How does Story #2 (suffering → glory) light up our world now?

John 9:35-39

[35] Jesus heard that they had thrown him out, and when he found him, he said, "Do you believe in the Son of Man?" [36] "Who is he, sir?" the man asked. "Tell me so that I may believe in him." [37] Jesus said, "You have now seen him; in fact, he is the one speaking with you." [38] Then the man said, "Lord, I believe," and he worshiped him. [39] Jesus said, "For judgment I have come into this world, so that the blind will see and those who see will become blind."

21. In what new way is Jesus now a light to the formerly blind man?

22. What does Jesus' spiritual light mean for our lives?

SECTION 5: The Disciples Learn to Love 10 mins

Acts 3:1-10—Peter Heals a Crippled Beggar

1 One day Peter and John were going up to the temple at the time of prayer—at three in the afternoon. 2 Now a man who was lame from birth was being carried to the temple gate called Beautiful, where he was put every day to beg from those going into the temple courts. 3 When he saw Peter and John about to enter, he asked them for money. 4 Peter looked straight at him, as did John. Then Peter said, "Look at us!" 5 So the man gave them his attention, expecting to get something from them. 6 Then Peter said, "Silver or gold I do not have, but what I do have I give you. In the name of Jesus Christ of Nazareth, walk." 7 Taking him by the right hand, he helped him up, and instantly the man's feet and ankles became strong. 8 He jumped to his feet and began to walk. Then he went with them into the temple courts, walking and jumping, and praising God. 9 When all the people saw him walking and praising God, 10 they recognized him as the same man who used to sit begging at the temple gate called Beautiful, and they were filled with wonder and amazement at what had happened to him.

23. How is this incident similar to the John 9 account?

24. How is this incident different from John 9? What have the disciples learned by watching Jesus?

Insight:

Just before his death, and again after his resurrection, Jesus promises to send the Holy Spirit to bring the mind and heart of Jesus into the disciples, enabling them to act like Jesus. So, in a very real sense, Jesus is doing the healing. He is now in the hearts of thousands of people. Not only is Jesus the power for love, but he is also in us, loving through us when we become his followers.

LESSON 5 APPLICATION

1. What did the Spirit help you see about either Jesus or yourself through this lesson?

A "Harmed" Daughter (Paul Miller)

I don't know the answer to all the suffering, but I do know that I've seen Jesus bring glory to God and save our family in the same way he did the blind man.

Jill and I were down at Children's Hospital of Philadelphia in 2001 doing some testing for our daughter Kim who is affected by multiple disabilities. The doctor said about Kim, "We don't know why." Jill said, "We know why. God sent her to keep our family from harm."

How? He humbled us. God gave us Kim to keep us *from all harm*…to keep us from being so self-righteous and "together." God used Kim to bring us to the end of ourselves, to teach us about love and to teach us about himself. Our lives no longer worked—we had to learn how to live from the bottom up. Like the blind man, we found glory in a most unexpected place.

When God gave us Kim, he gave us something we loved very much but couldn't control. She constantly drained our reserves. Jill and I are naturally quick, confident—and judgmental.

Once, before Kim was born, Jill was washing the car in our driveway and our neighbor passed on the sidewalk. A young mother herself, she said to Jill, "I don't know how you have the strength to do everything that you do." Jill replied, "If you're organized, you can get a lot done. You should try it."

Years ago, I was in downtown Philadelphia with a friend and a street person passed us. He slurred out something incomprehensible to me, and I dismissed him. As we were walking away my friend asked me, "Why did you talk to him like that? He just wanted to know where the soup kitchen was."

I smile at the work of God displayed in our lives, at God's sense of humor. Jill and I have spent countless hours with Kim doing speech therapy, helping her articulate her slurred words. I've spent hundreds of hours programming Kim's speech computer, which she is very proficient at. Jill no longer has time to be organized. When I ask her where some money has gone, she smiles at me and tells me that she doesn't know. She has sworn off being organized. "I just can't do it anymore."

What was our need? How were we blind? We were two self-reliant people who could do life on their own. What was God's gift? He overwhelmed us so that we'd see how dependent we were on him. God's glory has come into our life in some very unexpected ways.[2]

2. In this story, how does sin specifically lead to suffering in Paul's life? That is, how do you see the sowing and reaping principle worked out in his life?

---

[2] Miller, *Love Walked Among Us*, 40-41.

3. How do you see sowing and reaping in Jill's life?

4. In the same story, how does their suffering lead to God's glory, the *J-Curve*?

5. The disciples and the Pharisees wrongly applied the principle of sowing and reaping to the blind man's situation. Can you think of any Old Testament stories where the law was applied wrongly? Stories from your own life?

6. Recount at least one way that sin has led to suffering in your own life.

7. How has suffering led to glory in your life? Share a story with the group as you feel comfortable.

8. How has Jesus shown himself as the "light of the world" in your life? Fill in the chart below.

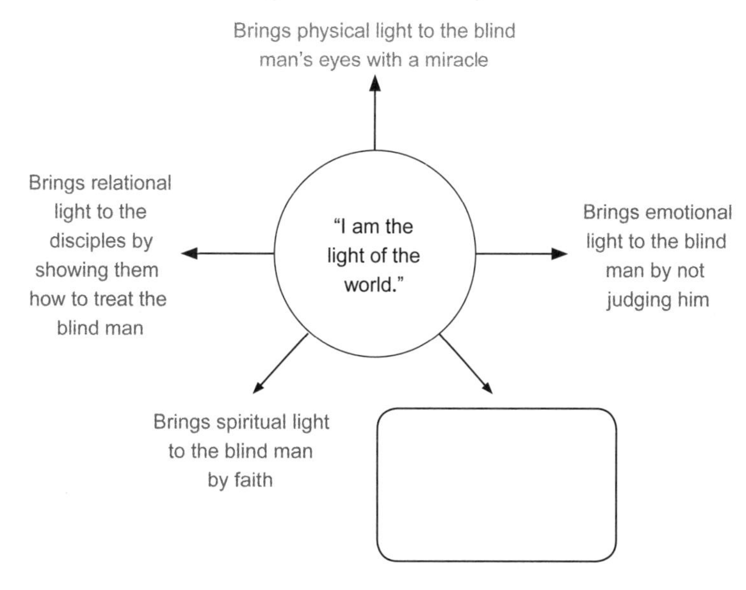

LESSON 5 ADDENDUM

Are the Miracles of Jesus True?

Modern Culture:

The ruling elites of our culture all but deny the existence of the supernatural. Privately, many people believe in God, but our culture demands that we keep our beliefs quiet. This practical atheism of our modern world is very unusual because almost every other culture since the dawn of time has assumed the existence of the supernatural world. If something (such as the supernatural) is not part of our mental framework, then it strikes us as weird. So I want to pause and ask the question, "Are the miracles of Jesus true? Did this incident really happen?" [*Once you deny the supernatural, then you deny the possibility of a miracle happening. But then you are left with having to make sense of the accounts of miracles in the Gospels.*] The answer that some give is that these stories about Jesus are myths. Let's test that by using Einstein's observation about Jesus. Einstein was asked:

Q. You accept the historical existence of Jesus?
A. Unquestionably. No man can read the Gospels without feeling the actual presence of Jesus. His personality pulsates in every word. No myth is filled with such life. How different, for instance, is the impression which we receive from an account of the legendary heroes of antiquity like Theseus! Theseus and other heroes of his type lack the authentic vitality of Jesus.[3]

Let's do what Einstein did and compare the myth of Theseus with John 9. Let's review the ancient texts side by side.

The Myth of Theseus

The god of the sea, Poseidon, sent a gift of a pure white bull to the king and queen of Minos, the modern island of Crete just below Greece. He wanted them to sacrifice the bull to him. But Queen Pasiphae was so taken by the beauty of the bull that she refused to kill it. Poseidon was so angered by this that he caused the Queen to give birth to a monster called the Minotaur, who was half man (bottom) and half bull (top). (It must have been a rough delivery!) Their architect, Daedalus, constructed a clever labyrinth under their palace at Thebes, out of which no one could ever hope to find his way. There they placed the Minotaur. The Minoans were forced to conquer other nations in order to feed the monster.

Athens had been conquered by the Minoans (who were from the island of Crete). Every

[3] S. Viereck questions Albert Einstein (1879-1955) in *The Saturday Evening Post*, Oct. 26, 1929.

nine years they demanded seven Athenian maidens and seven Athenian young men to be given as sacrifices to the Minotaur. The time came to send the young men and women to be eaten by the Minotaur. Theseus, the Athenian king's adopted son, offered to go in the place of one of the young men. The king begged him not to go, but Theseus demanded that he be allowed to do so. He promised his father that he would do everything he could to kill the Minotaur and escape from Thebes. If he were successful, he would sail home with a white sail, but if he were killed, the crew was instructed to use a black sail.

So Theseus and the chosen young men and maidens sailed for Crete. Upon their arrival they were put in jail, but Ariadne, the daughter of the king of Crete, came disguised into the jail and gave Theseus a magic ball of thread, which she had gotten from the architect Daedalus. When Theseus was put in the labyrinth, he would be able to find his way out with this ball of thread if he were first able to kill the Minotaur. Ariadne took him to the labyrinth at midnight and the ball of thread unwound of its own accord, leading him to the monster. He jumped on its back and strangled it. Then he followed the thread out of the maze, released his fellow prisoners, and sailed for home. Every day, Theseus's father was waiting high on a cliff for the return of the ship. When he finally saw the ship he gave a cry of despair and leaped to his death—Theseus had forgotten to change the sail.

	THESEUS	**BLIND MAN**
Which story is more real? Why?		
What is the miracle?		
How does the supernatural function? Is it expected?		
What are the different emotional responses to the miracle?		
Are there any authentic details?		

What kind of characters emerge?		
Which one reads like something that could happen today? Why?		
How does the god of the story (Poseidon or God, respectively) appear? How does he make himself known?		
How does the god of the story (Poseidon or God) relate to suffering?		

Insight: The Difference Between the Gospels and Myth

When we read a myth or a legend, we instinctively understand that we are in the world of fable. We "switch gears" when we read it; in the words of the poet Coleridge, we "suspend disbelief." But the Gospels are set in a real world of needs: wine running out at a wedding; hungry crowds with scant food; fruitless fishing trips; and empty money bags for the tax. Into this world quietly breaks the miraculous, which seems as ordinary as the hassles. In myth, extraordinary people in an extraordinary world do extraordinary things. In the Gospels, the extraordinary love and compassion of a remarkable yet very real man radiates and illuminates an ordinary world.[4]

The difference between the miracles in Theseus and in John 9. Both stories include supernatural or miraculous events. In the Theseus tale, the ball of thread and the half-man, half-bull are miraculous. In the story of the blind man, a man's sight is restored. But the similarities end there.

The Theseus tale imbeds the miraculous features, without comment, in the story itself. When Theseus is in Athens he doesn't say, "Hey guys, this is ridiculous: half-bull men don't exist." Or when he gets the magic ball of thread he doesn't say, "Are you sure this is going to work? How do I know you aren't pulling my leg?" He just accepts it as if magic balls of thread were everyday things. The miraculous seamlessly weaves through the story. On the other hand, in the story of the blind man, the miracle is a shock, and everyone reacts as if it is an extraordinary event. The whole story revolves

---

[4] Miller, *Love Walked Among Us*, 17.

around the introduction of the miraculous. As the blind man says, "Nobody has ever heard of opening the eyes of a man born blind." Put another way, one story seems unreal because it treats the odd as ordinary, whereas the other seems real because it treats the miraculous as odd.

The difference extends to the emotional responses of the characters. Since Theseus accepts the miracles as ordinary, he gives no emotional response to them. The miracle is a part of nature, much like the sun coming up. But in the story of the blind man, responses range from disbelief and denial to calm acceptance. The neighbors are puzzled, the parents are fearful, the religious officials are perplexed and angry, and the blind man is thankful and almost amused at the people scratching their heads.

Sometimes the details of a story give us a clue that something is not real. For instance, Theseus might have forgotten to change the sail if Athens were a quick trip from Crete, but it is a journey of several days. At some point, one of the fourteen on board would surely have noticed that they had the wrong sail up. And how does a half-man, half-bull eat people? Cows can't eat flesh; they don't have the teeth for it. In contrast, the details in the account of the blind man give it a rich, lifelike authenticity. You can see Jesus spitting on the ground, making mud, and putting it on the man's eyes.

Finally, what kinds of characters emerge? Theseus, the classic Greek hero, is virtually indistinguishable from similar figures, such as Hercules. Like other mythical heroes, Theseus never doubts he'll come home. Only egomaniacs or the mentally ill never doubt. Even Jesus experiences anguish when facing his own death. Whereas Theseus is plastic, the characters in the biblical story are all people you can relate to. People haven't changed much in 2,000 years!

LESSON 6: SELF-RIGHTEOUSNESS

OUTLINE:

1. A Sinful Woman Crashes a Party. . . . . 10 mins
2. The Scene from Simon's Perspective. . . . . 5 mins
3. Jesus Loves the Woman . . . . 10 mins
4. Jesus Responds . . . . 10 mins
5. Forgiving Sins . . . . 10 mins

LESSON 6: SELF-RIGHTEOUSNESS

SECTION 1: A Sinful Woman Crashes a Party 10 mins

Luke 7:36-50—Jesus Anointed by a Sinful Woman

36 When one of the Pharisees invited Jesus to have dinner with him, he went to the Pharisee's house and reclined at the table. 37 A woman in that town who lived a sinful life learned that Jesus was eating at the Pharisee's house, so she came there with an alabaster jar of perfume. 38 As she stood behind him at his feet weeping, she began to wet his feet with her tears. Then she wiped them with her hair, kissed them and poured perfume on them.

39 When the Pharisee who had invited him saw this, he said to himself, "If this man were a prophet, he would know who is touching him and what kind of woman she is—that she is a sinner."

40 Jesus answered him, "Simon, I have something to tell you."

"Tell me, teacher," he said.

41 "Two people owed money to a certain moneylender. One owed him five hundred denarii, and the other fifty. 42 Neither of them had the money to pay him back, so he forgave the debts of both. Now which of them will love him more?"

43 Simon replied, "I suppose the one who had the bigger debt forgiven."

"You have judged correctly," Jesus said.

44 Then he turned toward the woman and said to Simon, "Do you see this woman? I came into your house. You did not give me any water for my feet, but she wet my feet with her tears and wiped them with her hair. 45 You did not give me a kiss, but this woman, from the time I entered, has not stopped kissing my feet. 46 You did not put oil on my head, but she has poured perfume on my feet. 47 Therefore, I tell you, her many sins have been forgiven—as her great love has shown. But whoever has been forgiven little loves little."

48 Then Jesus said to her, "Your sins are forgiven."

49 The other guests began to say among themselves, "Who is this who even forgives sins?"

50 Jesus said to the woman, "Your faith has saved you; go in peace."

Historical Background: Details of the Story

- The Greek feast custom was to lie with one's left elbow on a cushion at a low table, feet pointing outward. The table was U-shaped, so servants could enter the U to serve the food.[1]

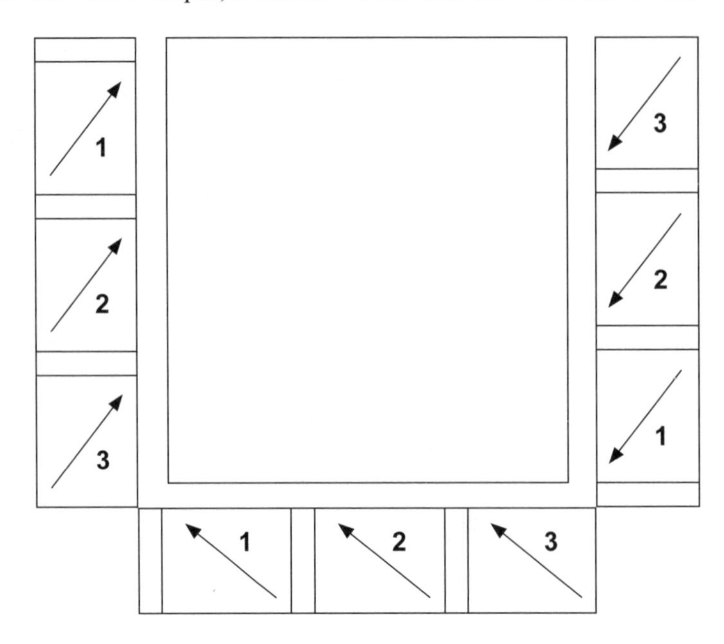

- The Jewish custom for everyday meals was to sit at a high table. But Jews usually adopted the Greek custom for feasts.
- Foot washing was vital because people wore open sandals and walked along dusty or muddy roads.
- Bathing was infrequent, and there was no deodorant. Women typically hung small alabaster jars of perfume around their necks to perfume themselves.
- It is possible the description of the woman as a "sinner" means she's a prostitute. It could also mean she has committed adultery multiple times. That is, she's a marriage wrecker.[2]

---

1 We have permission from Dr. Struck (forwarded to Paul on 2.23.19) to reproduce this diagram. Struck's depiction of the triclinium seating arrangement, reproduced here, is the prevalent one. Even some of the (reconstructed) figures found at Pompeii reflect the same triclinium arrangement.

The question of a table's placement (raised by Edersheim) doesn't negate the typical arrangement of the triclinium, but helpfully complements it. Dennis Smith says that couches were of various designs and held different numbers of people. What's important (per Smith) is the position of the person of honor (as indicated on Struck's diagram). See Dennis Smith, "Greco-Roman Meal Customs," pages 650-652 in the Anchor Bible Dictionary: Volume 4 (K-N). Ed. David Noel Freedman. (New York: Doubleday, 1992).

2 Alfred Plummer, "The Woman That Was a Sinner," *Expository Times* 27 (1915): 42.

SECTION 2: The Scene from Simon's Perspective 5 mins

Jesus Simon

Woman

1. How does Simon relate to Jesus?

Historical Background: Greeting Guests

In ancient Near Eastern culture, a well-known rabbi was to be greeted with a kiss, have oil poured on his head, and have his feet washed. Simon's greeting of Jesus (or lack thereof) was a slap in the face. It would be like inviting someone for dinner and telling him to clean your bathroom when he arrived.

2. What does Simon mean when he says, "If this man were a prophet…"?

Insight:

Having heard the reports regarding the widow of Nain's son, Simon is likely investigating Jesus. Is he a prophet—someone who sees from God's viewpoint and speaks God's words? Simon presumes he is not, since he appears not to see the woman for what she is.

3. How does Simon relate to the woman?

4. Who is a worse sinner: Simon or the woman?

5. What is the difference between their sins?

Insight:

Simon's self-righteousness is obvious to us, but it was not obvious to him. In the same way, it is hard to see our own self-righteousness.

SECTION 3: Jesus Loves the Woman — 10 mins

6. This woman crashes a party in order to see Jesus. Why do you think she is drawn to him?

7. What does she do to express her love for Jesus?

Historical Background: A Woman's Hair

In this world, and many traditional cultures now, a woman lets down her hair only in private with her husband. Doing so in public was the cultural equivalent of going topless on a family-friendly beach.[3]

8. Given this cultural context, what kind of man would not be bothered by this woman's behavior?

[3] Kenneth Bailey recounts the following description of the regulations for stoning and immoral woman: "The priest seizes her garment, it does not matter if they are rent or torn open, until he uncovers her bosom and loosens her hair. [But] Rabbi Judah said: if her bosom was beautiful he did not expose it, and if her hair was comely, he did not loosen it" (*b. Sanh. 45a; cf. also b. Sotah 81*). He concludes: "Clearly the rabbis considered uncovering the bosom and loosening the hair to be acts that fall in the same category" Kenneth Bailey, *Through Peasant Eyes*, 9.

9. Let's contrast how Simon and Jesus treat the woman.

JESUS	SIMON

10. How would you feel if she came into your luncheon and started crying over you, wiping your feet with her hair?

11. Why would you be embarrassed? If you were a man, what would concern you?

12. Would you feel shamed or honored by her behavior? Why?

13. Where is Jesus on the scale?

14. Why isn't Jesus uncomfortable with how close and personal she is? What does this tell us about him?

SECTION 4: Jesus Responds — 10 mins

15. What does Jesus do with his body in verse 44 that he has done in the other accounts we've studied?

16. How do Jesus' words to Simon in that verse reinforce what his body is doing?

17. Why do you think Jesus turns toward the woman and tells Simon to look at her at the same time?

Insight:

Jesus looks at the woman in order to help Simon see. He's showing Simon how to look at her so he can love her. He is teaching Simon how a prophet—in fact, how God—sees people. Jesus' body language mirrors his teaching.

18. What three things does Jesus say that Simon did wrong? What three things does the woman do right?

SIMON	WOMAN
↓	↑
↓	↑
↓	↑

19. What is Jesus doing for the woman when he rebukes Simon?

20. In Luke 2:34, an old man named Simeon tells Jesus' mother Mary that Jesus is "appointed for the fall and rising of many in Israel." How do we see that prophecy fulfilled in this scene?

Insight: Seeing the Big Picture

Simon judges Jesus because Jesus is supposed to be a prophet who sees people from God's point of view. In Simon's mind, Jesus can't be a prophet because he doesn't see what this woman is really like. In fact, the woman does see what she is like—that's why she is weeping. Jesus, as a true prophet of God, sees not only why she's weeping but also what Simon is really like. Simon can't see what he's really like, how needy he is, so he's unable to see the woman. To help Simon see her, as well as himself, Jesus first tells him a story. Then Jesus teaches him how to look at the woman by looking at her himself while he tells Simon to do the same. Finally, Jesus compares Simon's behavior with the woman's. Jesus is a prophet unlike any other.

SECTION 5: Forgiving Sins — 10 mins

21. First, does the woman need forgiveness?

Insight: Adultery

In the Sermon on the Mount, Jesus declares that we can commit adultery in our hearts by how we look at a person (Matthew 5:27, 28). In so doing, he affirms and strengthens the Old Testament prohibition against adultery.

22. How, in this story, does Jesus indicate that adultery is wrong?

23. What is odd about Jesus telling the woman, "Your sins are forgiven"?

Historical Background: Forgiving Sins

British scholar N. T. Wright compares Jesus' forgiveness of this woman to "a private individual approaching you on the street and offering to issue you a passport or a driver's license—or, perhaps more appropriately in this case, a private individual approaching a prisoner in a jail and offering him a royal pardon, signed by himself."[4]

24. Look at verse 49. Are the other guests pleased about this forgiveness?

Insight: Forgiveness

- When Jesus forgives the sins of a paralyzed man, the Pharisees rage, "Why does this fellow talk like that? He's blaspheming! Who can forgive sins but God alone?" (Mark 2:7).
- Jesus' forgiveness makes sense only if the woman has sinned against him. She has only sinned against him if he is God, the creator of the moral law.
- Jesus speaks with an authority belonging to God alone, revealing himself as God's Son.

25. What immediately happens to Jesus' reputation because he loves this woman?

Gospel Connection:

Jesus' love for her and its effect on him foreshadow how he forgives sins.

---

[4] N. T. Wright, *Jesus and the Victory of God* (Minneapolis, MN: Fortress Press, 1996), 435.

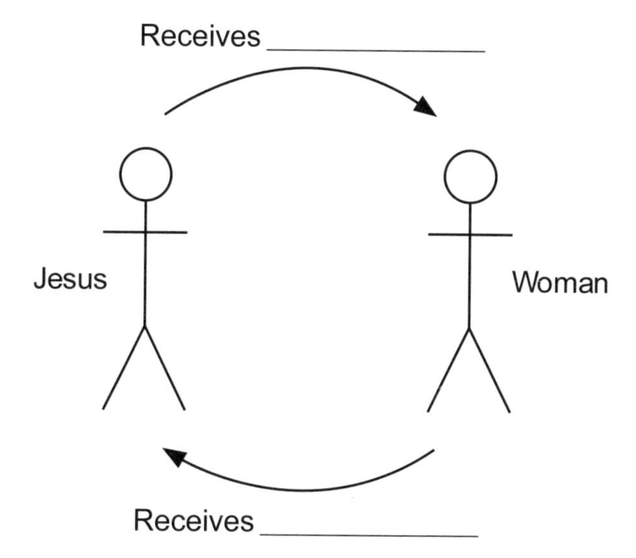

- Being compassionate to the woman means that Jesus takes upon himself the curse society has put on her. This kind of exchange always happens when we love. It's the heart of Jesus' saving work on the cross. "He redeemed us from the curse of the law by becoming a curse for us" (Galatians 3:13).
- Jesus forgiving the woman is like him bailing her out of bankruptcy with a billion dollar personal check; he covers her losses himself. At the cross, he puts the money behind the check. In other words, the mini-substitution in this story looks forward to Jesus' substitution of his life for the sins of the world. And so, Jesus' words, "Your sins are forgiven," are an offer to everyone.
- Jesus offers the very thing we need instead of our self-righteousness: his perfect righteousness! When we accept God's forgiveness through Christ, we can abandon the sense of moral superiority that prevents us from loving others.

LESSON 6 APPLICATION

1. What did the Spirit help you see about either Jesus or yourself through this lesson?

Read the following story of Simon Wiesenthal's struggle to forgive.[5]

In 1944, [Simon] Wiesenthal was a young Polish prisoner of the Nazis. He watched as Nazi soldicrs killed his grandmother and forced his mother into a freight car crammed with elderly Jewish women. Altogether, eighty-nine of his Jewish relatives would die at the hands of the Nazis. Wiesenthal himself tried to commit suicide when first captured.

One sunny day as Wiesenthal's prison detail was cleaning rubbish out of a German hospital, a nurse approached him. "Are you a Jew?" she asked hesitantly, then signaled him to accompany her. Apprehensive, Wiesenthal followed her until they reached a dark room where a lone soldier lay swathed in bandages. White gauze covered the man's face, with openings cut out for a mouth, nose, and ears.

The nurse disappeared, leaving him alone with the spectral figure. The wounded man was an SS officer, and he had summoned Wiesenthal for a deathbed confession. "My name is Karl," said a raspy voice from somewhere within the bandages. "I must tell you of this horrible deed—tell you because you are a Jew."

Karl began his story by reminiscing about his Catholic upbringing and childhood faith, which he lost in the Hitler Youth Corps. He later served the SS with distinction and had only recently returned, wounded, from the Russian front. Three times as Karl tried to tell the story, Wiesenthal tried to leave. But the officer begged him to listen.

In the town of Dnyepropetrovsk, abandoned by the retreating Russians, Karl's unit stumbled onto booby traps that killed thirty of their soldiers. To retaliate, they herded three hundred Jews into a house, doused it with gasoline, and fired grenades at it. Karl and his men encircled the house, guns drawn to shoot anyone who tried to escape.

"The screams were horrible," he said, reliving the moment. "I saw a man with a small child in his arms. His clothes were alight. By his side stood a woman, doubtless the mother of the child. With his free hand the man covered the child's eyes, then he jumped into the street. Seconds later the mother followed. Then from the other windows fell burning bodies. We shot … Oh God!"

Wiesenthal sat in silence, letting the German soldier describe other atrocities. At last Karl concluded, "I am left here with my guilt." He went on: "In the last hours of my life you are with me. I do not know who you are, I know only that you are a Jew and that is enough. I know that what I have

---

[5] Adapted from Philip Yancey's *What's So Amazing about Grace?* (Grand Rapids, MI: Zondervan, 2002), 109-110.

told you is terrible. In the long nights while I have been waiting for death, time and time again I have longed to talk about it to a Jew and beg forgiveness from him.... I know what I am asking is almost too much for you, but without your answer I cannot die in peace."

Simon Wiesenthal felt the immense crushing burden of his race bear down on him. He stared out the window at the sunlit courtyard. He looked at the eyeless heap of bandages lying in the bed..."At last I made up my mind," Wiesenthal writes, "and without a word I left the room."

2. What do you think about what Wiesenthal did?

3. What similarities do you see between Simon the Pharisee and Simon Wiesenthal?

4. How is Jesus different from both Simons?

5. Where do you struggle with self-righteousness? What kind of standards do you make for yourself (or others) in that area?

6. How does understanding God's forgiveness and acceptance break down the need to be "right" or "superior" in that area for you?

7. How could Jesus' style of relating help you with a difficult person in your life?

8. Reread Luke 4:36-50. Reflect upon how "seeing" ties together this whole incident:
    a. *Simon believes Jesus can't be a prophet because Jesus is "blind" to what?*
    b. *What does the woman see about herself and about Jesus?*
    c. *What does Jesus see about the woman and about Simon?*
    d. *Who is the real blind person in this story? Why?*

9. Describe a relationship where self-righteousness blocked you from compassion. What first step toward compassion could you take this week? Ask the Father for the Spirit's help!

LESSON 7:
SELF-RIGHTEOUSNESS AND GRACE

OUTLINE:

1. The Pharisee and the Tax Collector . . . . 15 mins
2. Self-Esteem or Grace? . . . . 10 mins
3. The Parable of the Lost Son . . . . 15 mins
4. The Human Heart and Grace . . . . 5 mins

LESSON 7: SELF-RIGHTEOUSNESS AND GRACE

SECTION 1: The Pharisee and the Tax Collector 15 mins

Luke 18:9-14—The Parable of the Pharisee and the Tax Collector

9 To some who were confident of their own righteousness and looked down on everyone else, Jesus told this parable: **10** "Two men went up to the temple to pray, one a Pharisee and the other a tax collector. **11** The Pharisee stood by himself and prayed: 'God, I thank you that I am not like other people—robbers, evildoers, adulterers—or even like this tax collector. **12** I fast twice a week and give a tenth of all I get.'

13 "But the tax collector stood at a distance. He would not even look up to heaven, but beat his breast and said, 'God, have mercy on me, a sinner.'

14 "I tell you that this man, rather than the other, went home justified before God. For all those who exalt themselves will be humbled, and those who humble themselves will be exalted."

Historical Background: Tax Collectors

The Roman government auctioned the job of tax collector to the highest bidder. The tax collector first paid Rome for taxation rights to a region. Then he collected taxes from the people living there. Tax collectors could, and typically did, exact more than what they paid Rome—essentially stealing from their fellow citizens. In Judea, tax collectors were as disreputable as prostitutes. The rabbis called them robbers. But not only were they thieves, they were also agents of the occupying Roman government and a constant reminder of the people's captivity.[1]

[1] T. E. Schmidt, "Taxes" in *Dictionary of Jesus and the Gospels*. Eds. Joel B. Green and Scot McKnight (Downers Grove, IL: InterVarsity Press, 1992), 805.

	PHARISEE	TAX COLLECTOR
What do we know of his past life from his prayer? (Positive or negative.)		
Does he have any needs in his life?		
Where does he look for his security? What is his source of change?		
How does he see himself? Describe his self-image.		
What kind of behavior does his self-image lead to as he prays?		
How does it affect his physical posture: how he talks and looks?		
What is his attitude toward God?		
Which one is God pleased with?		

SECTION 2: Self-Esteem or Grace? 10 mins

1. **What are some common phrases describing how you should feel about yourself?**

2. **What do all these phrases assume about the self? Is it basically good or basically bad?**

3. **Does the Pharisee have good or bad self-esteem? How can you tell?**

4. **What about the tax collector? How is his self-esteem?**

Insight: Self-Esteem vs. Grace

- The self-esteem movement is the opposite of grace. Self-esteem is my power helping me feel good about myself. The end, or goal, of self-esteem is self-righteousness. By this standard, the Pharisee has "arrived"!
- Grace is God's power coming into my emptiness, offering forgiveness, cleansing, and hope. The tax collector is asking for grace.

5. **Look back at verse 14. Which man goes home "justified"?**

6. **What's the danger of emphasizing self-esteem?**

7. **How does seeing oneself as a sinner, like the tax collector, actually confer dignity on a person?**

 **Modern Culture:**

Interestingly, psychologists are having second thoughts about the self-esteem movement.[2] Guess which segment of the population has the highest self-esteem? Criminals![3] Focusing on our own goodness actually makes us more demanding and difficult rather than more loving. Instead of a vision of how good we are, we need a vision of how bad we are, intertwined with a vision of God's grace.

8. What's the point of the parable? Where does self-esteem and self-righteousness get us?

SECTION 3: The Parable of the Lost Son — 15 mins

Luke 15:25-32

> [25] "Meanwhile, the older son was in the field. When he came near the house, he heard music and dancing. [26] So he called one of the servants and asked him what was going on. [27] 'Your brother has come,' he replied, 'and your father has killed the fattened calf because he has him back safe and sound.'
>
> [28] "The older brother became angry and refused to go in. So his father went out and pleaded with him. [29] But he answered his father, 'Look! All these years I've been slaving for you and never disobeyed your orders. Yet you never gave me even a young goat so I could celebrate with my friends. [30] But when this son of yours who has squandered your property with prostitutes comes home, you kill the fattened calf for him!'
>
> [31] "'My son,' the father said, 'you are always with me, and everything I have is yours. [32] But we had to celebrate and be glad, because this brother of yours was dead and is alive again; he was lost and is found.'"

---

[2] John P. Hewett, *The Myth of Self-Esteem: Finding Happiness and Solving Problems in America* (New York: St. Martin's Press, 1998).

[3] Roy F. Baumeister, Laura Smart, and Joseph M. Boden. "Relation of Threatened Egotism to Violence and Aggression: The Dark Side of High Self-Esteem," *Psychological Review 103.1 (1996)*, 5-33.

	OLDER BROTHER	YOUNGER BROTHER
What has he done with his time the last few years? What hasn't he been doing?		
What is his attitude toward his father's grace?		
What is his heart like? Proud or broken?		

9. What is Jesus commending? What is he condemning?

10. What does the elder son hate about his father's grace?

11. What does the older brother fail to see about the younger brother?

12. What does the older brother fail to see about himself?

13. How does his anger show in the words he uses?

14. Given what we know about ancient Near Eastern culture, what does the older brother's refusal to enter the feast communicate?

Historical Background: Respect for the Father

The older son publicly insults his father in front of the entire village[4] when he refuses to enter the feast. Disrespect toward authority in a patriarchal system is one of the gravest offenses. To this day, in some parts of Asia, younger brothers must stand out of respect when their older brother enters the room. How much more should a father be honored!

15. Let's review for a moment: Why does the older brother struggle to extend grace to his younger brother?

16. In what sense is the younger brother doing better than his older brother?

17. What's the point of the parable? How does real change begin to happen in us?

SECTION 4: The Human Heart and Grace — 5 mins

18. How are Simon (the Pharisee from the last lesson) and the older brother from this lesson similar?

---

4 We know the feast was for the whole village because the fattened calf was slaughtered. In an era with no refrigeration, the calf had to be eaten that day, meaning the whole village would be invited. See Kenneth Bailey, *Through Peasant Eyes*, 186.

19. Why is it hard to admit we need grace?

Insight: "Amazing Grace"

- The heart of our rebellion against God is the desire to be on our own, to be independent of God. Receiving grace means telling God, "I surrender. I cannot 'do life' on my own."
- Many people don't realize how countercultural the well-known hymn "Amazing Grace" actually is. It admits we have failed and need God's grace to change us.

> Amazing grace, how sweet the sound
> That saved a wretch like me.
> I once was lost but now am found
> Was blind but now I see.
>
> 'Twas grace that taught my heart to fear
> And grace my fears relieved.
> How precious did that grace appear
> The hour I first believed.[5]

20. What's freeing about realizing we're a mess?

21. How does giving up our self-righteousness and accepting God's grace free us to love?

Insight:

The key to love is realizing you don't have it all together. When you see your need for forgiveness and mercy, then you cry out to God. Not only does God forgive you, but he also changes your heart so you no longer feel superior to others.

---

[5] "Amazing Grace," John Newton, 1772.

LESSON 7 APPLICATION

1. What did the Spirit help you see about either Jesus or yourself through this lesson?

2. Imagine you are the tax collector from the Luke 18 parable. Find a private place and re-enact his cry to God from verse 13. How did that feel? Now read verse 14. How did that feel?

3. Share with the group one way you have "bought in" to the self-esteem movement.

4. Do you believe you need grace? Why or why not? Write a prayer expressing your feelings to God.

5. Which character in the Parable of the Lost Son—the father, the older son, or the younger son—is easiest for you to understand? Hardest? Why?

6. What does this suggest to you about your own relationship to self-righteousness and grace?

7. Recall a time when you, like the elder brother, despised the grace someone else received. Why did you respond the way you did? What truth from this lesson helps you reframe that situation?

LESSON 8: LEGALISM

OUTLINE:

1. Jesus Reacts to Legalism . . . . 10 mins
2. Legalism Destroys Love . . . . 10 mins
3. Jesus' Teaching about the Heart . . . . 10 mins
4. The False Hope of Rules . . . . 5 mins
5. Beautiful but Broken . . . . 5 mins
6. Jesus Offers Hope . . . . 5 mins

LESSON 8: LEGALISM

SECTION 1: Jesus Reacts to Legalism — 10 mins

1. **Every culture has rules that become legalistic, that forget about the person. For instance, what does our culture say about women—what they should be like and what they should do with their lives?**

2. **How do these rules make you feel?**

3. **How have you seen legalism in your family or in society as a whole?**

Luke 11:37-43—Jesus Reacts to Legalism

[37] When Jesus had finished speaking, a Pharisee invited him to eat with him; so he went in and reclined at the table. [38] But the Pharisee was surprised when he noticed that Jesus did not first wash before the meal.

[39] Then the Lord said to him, "Now then, you Pharisees clean the outside of the cup and dish, but inside you are full of greed and wickedness. [40] You foolish people! Did not the one who made the outside make the inside also? [41] But now as for what is inside you—be generous to the poor, and everything will be clean for you.

[42] "Woe to you Pharisees, because you give God a tenth of your mint, rue and all other kinds of garden herbs, but you neglect justice and the love of God. You should have practiced the latter without leaving the former undone.

[43] "Woe to you Pharisees, because you love the most important seats in the synagogues and respectful greetings in the marketplaces.

4. What do you think of Jesus' reaction? Remember, he's a guest at someone's house and the Pharisees have merely expressed surprise that he didn't wash his hands.

Historical Background: Ritual Washing

Jesus' response makes sense when we realize that this type of washing was not about cleanliness. They didn't know germs existed! Ritual washing was a rule—one not in the Bible—that had become central to the Pharisees' whole way of thinking and relating.

5. What image or picture does Jesus use in 11:39 to explain what's wrong with the Pharisees' legalism?

6. What does Jesus mean when he says, "You Pharisees clean the outside of the cup and dish, but inside you are full of greed and wickedness"?

7. Picture what Jesus is saying about how the Pharisees wash their cups. What's humorous about his observation?

Historical Background: Tithing

Jesus describes the Pharisees' tithing habits as an example of how they "wash the outside of the cup." Tithing is the ancient practice of giving 10% of one's income to God. The Pharisees scrupulously gave one out of every ten mint leaves to God. But they neglected Scripture's commands in more important matters, like practicing justice and loving God.

8. Jesus uses the cup to convey two different truths. What is the second truth in this statement: "But give what is inside to the poor, and everything will be clean for you"?

Insight:

Jesus calls the Pharisees to replace self-righteousness with real righteousness. Self-righteousness focuses on appearances, the outside of the cup. But real righteousness has integrity; the inside and outside are the same. The Pharisees miss the fact that the law is an invitation to uncalculated generosity and instead use it to measure their own goodness.[1]

---

[1] Margaret Atler, *Resurrection Psychology* (Chicago, IL: Loyola University Press, 1994), 32.

SECTION 2: Legalism Destroys Love 10 mins

Mark 7:1-13—Clean and Unclean

[1] The Pharisees and some of the teachers of the law who had come from Jerusalem gathered around Jesus [2] and saw some of his disciples eating food with hands that were defiled, that is, unwashed. [3] (The Pharisees and all the Jews do not eat unless they give their hands a ceremonial washing, holding to the tradition of the elders. [4] When they come from the marketplace they do not eat unless they wash. And they observe many other traditions, such as the washing of cups, pitchers and kettles.)

[5] So the Pharisees and teachers of the law asked Jesus, "Why don't your disciples live according to the tradition of the elders instead of eating their food with defiled hands?"

[6] He replied, "Isaiah was right when he prophesied about you hypocrites; as it is written:

"'These people honor me with their lips,
but their hearts are far from me.
[7] They worship me in vain;
their teachings are merely human rules.'

[8] You have let go of the commands of God and are holding on to human traditions."

[9] And he continued, "You have a fine way of setting aside the commands of God in order to observe your own traditions! [10] For Moses said, 'Honor your father and mother,' and, 'Anyone who curses their father or mother is to be put to death.' [11] But you say that if anyone declares that what might have been used to help their father or mother is Corban (that is, devoted to God)—[12] then you no longer let them do anything for their father or mother. [13] Thus you nullify the word of God by your tradition that you have handed down. And you do many things like that."

9. What does Jesus contrast in verses 8 and 9?

Historical Background: Tradition of the Elders

The tradition of the elders arose because the Pharisees idolized the law and wanted to protect against any possibility of disobeying it. They added more rules than were actually in the law so people wouldn't get close to disobeying the law. This is called "fencing the law," and it led them to miss the heart of the law which is love. In other words, God's law isn't wrong. But if we elevate human traditions to the level of God's law, we create legalism.

10. How do the Pharisees use legalism to destroy the heart of the law?

11. What is the heart of the law?

12. Why do the Pharisees enjoy their legalism? What good things does it do for them?

Principle: Legalism uses a good rule in a way that forgets about the person.

SECTION 3: Jesus' Teaching about the Heart 10 mins

Mark 7:14-15, 21-23

14 Again Jesus called the crowd to him and said, "Listen to me, everyone, and understand this. 15 Nothing outside a person can defile them by going into them. Rather, it is what comes out of a person that defiles them."

---

21 "For it is from within, out of a person's heart, that evil thoughts come—sexual immorality, theft, murder, 22 adultery, greed, malice, deceit, lewdness, envy, slander, arrogance and folly. 23 All these evils come from inside and defile a person."

13. What is surprising—even shocking—about what Jesus says?

Modern Culture:

Jesus' analysis seems overly pessimistic to our modern ears. Usually when we see great compassion, we sigh with relief and say, "My faith in humanity is restored." We think there must be a natural goodness in people. Once more, Jesus combines patterns of behavior that are so incongruent, they're startling.

14. Do you ever have to teach a child to do wrong? Can anyone give an example?

15. How does this confirm what Jesus is saying?

16. Imagine you had a video of everything you said, did, or thought. Then you accidentally lost it! How desperate would you be to find it?

Insight: What Legalism Assumes about People

Legalism assumes people are basically good, so all that is needed is external change. Follow a few rules and we have life solved. But if people aren't basically good, the problem is much deeper.

17. So what is the problem with legalism?

18. Why do we tend toward legalism?

19. Why does focusing on man-made rules fail to change us? Why isn't it enough to "clean the outside of the cup"?

Insight:

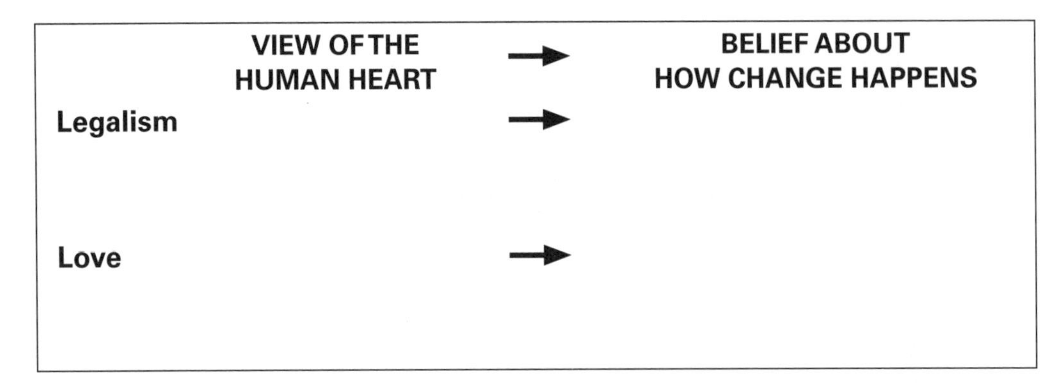

	VIEW OF THE HUMAN HEART	→	BELIEF ABOUT HOW CHANGE HAPPENS
Legalism		→	
Love		→	

SECTION 4: The False Hope of Rules — 5 mins

20. If you work out regularly, how do you feel when you see an overweight person? Or, if you adhere to a strict diet, what do you think about the coworker who eats fast food every day in the next cubicle?

21. How does the Pharisee feel when he counts the mint leaves on each plant, picks every tenth one, and takes them to the synagogue on the Sabbath?

22. What hint does that give as to why we become legalistic?

23. Can you think of something good you do that makes you feel better than other people? Each of us tends to do this.

Principle: Love looks at people in their need. Legalism wants people to look at you in your greatness.

24. How might our efforts at self-improvement (exercise, losing weight, healthy diet) be similar to the Pharisees' "cleaning the outside of the cup"?

Insight:

It's not wrong to exercise or eat a healthy diet, but we can use anything to elevate ourselves above other people. Legalism is:

- A false gospel that focuses on the bad news of other people's failures and the good news of our performance.
- Self-attainable.
- Much easier than love. It simplifies the world by substituting a system for the hard, humbling work of love.[2]

Matthew 23:5

> "Everything they do is done for man to see."

SECTION 5: Beautiful but Broken — 5 mins

25. How is Jesus' description of the heart both discouraging and encouraging?

Modern Culture: Unprepared for Life

Misunderstanding the nature of the human heart leaves us unprepared for life in some basic ways:

- Marriage: Those who enter marriage assuming the basic goodness of their spouse may be shocked to find out what he or she is really like. This is part of why divorce has become so commonplace.
- Parenting: Likewise, parents are surprised by how selfish their children can be.

---

[2] Remember how the disciples judged the blind man, assuming that sin caused his blindness? Earlier in John, Jesus healed a rather whiny lame man and sent him off with, "Stop sinning or something worse may happen to you" (John 5:14). Our modern legalism would like to simplify the world by denying the possibility that sin leads to illness. Jesus affirms the possibility.

Modern Culture: Cynicism about Human Nature

As people encounter life, they lose their naïve optimism and become cynical, assuming a selfish motive behind even good behavior. In a letter to Pastor Oskar Pfister, Sigmund Freud wrote, "I have found little that is 'good' about human beings on the whole. In my experience most of them are trash."[3] Freud's view holds out little hope for humankind. Ironically, our society rejects Jesus' view of the heart as too pessimistic and ends up with an even more pessimistic one![4]

SECTION 6: Jesus Offers Hope 5 mins

Insight:

The Bible balances two contrary impulses of the human heart: great evil and great beauty. While the world is condemned to swing between a naïve optimism that sees only beauty and a despairing pessimism that sees only brokenness, the Bible clearly discerns the problem and offers a solution: the gospel.

Mark 1:14-15—Jesus Preaches the Good News

14 After John was put in prison, Jesus went into Galilee, proclaiming the good news of God. **15** "The time has come," he said. "The kingdom of God has come near. Repent and believe the good news!"

Gospel Connection:

The Greek word that we often translate as "good news" can also be translated as "gospel." Gospel simply means "good news."

26. What two things does Jesus tell people they have to do?

Insight:

Repenting requires hearing the bad news about myself—that I am the problem. Then I can *believe* the good news that Jesus is the solution. The good news is that Jesus saves me from myself.

---

[3] Sigmund Freud and Oskar Pfister, *Psychoanalysis and Faith: The Letters of Sigmund Freud and Oskar Pfister*, trans. E. Mosbacher. Eds., H. Men and E. L. Freud. (New York: Basic, 1963), 61.

[4] In the 19th century, optimism prevailed among society's gatekeepers who believed in the goodness of the human heart and the progress of humanity through technology. The wars and strife of the 20th century left sociologists disillusioned, but popular culture still views people as basically good.

27. Think back to Jesus' parable of the Pharisee and tax collector in the last lesson. What does that story suggest about how we start repenting and believing? How do we change ourselves?

Insight:

We're not naturally compassionate. We can't love the way Jesus does. A good example—even Jesus himself—isn't enough. We need a new heart with the very person of Jesus in it. And that's exactly what Jesus does for us! That's why he came to die. That's what the gospel is all about.

LESSON 8 APPLICATION

1. What did the Spirit help you see about either Jesus or yourself through this lesson?

2. To find your "inner legalist," make a list of things you either are good at or tend to make mini-judgments of other people about. For example: dieting, exercise, laziness.

3. Pick one of the areas in question 2 above. What are your rules? How does your legalism make you feel better about yourself?

4. Share about a time when your legalism "forgot about" or hurt another person. What happened?

5. How is your legalism like washing only the outside of a cup?

6. In Luke 10:26-27, Matthew 22:34-40, and Mark 12:28-31, Jesus says the heart of the law is love. Read at least two of these passages and reflect on what you notice about the law.

7. To wash the inside of the cup, Jesus says we must "repent and believe." As the Spirit leads, write a short prayer of repentance for the legalism you identified above. Ask for faith in this area of your life.

8. Pick one person in your life. Reflect on how his or her life is both beautiful and broken.

9. Then consider your own life. How are you both beautiful and broken?

LESSON 9: RELATIONAL LEGALISM

OUTLINE:

1. Martha's Legalism . . . . 10 mins
2. Judas' Legalism. . . . . 10 mins
3. Our Legalism . . . . 5 mins
4. Idols. . . . . 15 mins
5. The Peculiar Blindness of the Legalist . . . . 5 mins

LESSON 9: RELATIONAL LEGALISM

SECTION 1: Martha's Legalism — 10 mins

Luke 10:38-42—Mary and Martha

[38] As Jesus and his disciples were on their way, he came to a village where a woman named Martha opened her home to him. [39] She had a sister called Mary, who sat at the Lord's feet listening to what he said. [40] But Martha was distracted by all the preparations that had to be made. She came to him and asked, "Lord, don't you care that my sister has left me to do the work by myself? Tell her to help me!"

[41] "Martha, Martha," the Lord answered, "you are worried and upset about many things, [42] but few things are needed—or indeed only one. Mary has chosen what is better, and it will not be taken away from her."

1. What's Martha like as a person? What clues does the story give us?

2. What's Mary like as a person? What clues does the story give us?

3. Why is Martha upset?

4. What good principle is on Martha's mind?

Historical Background: "Male Students Only"

Martha could also be upset because Mary is assuming the role of a male disciple of Jesus, which is suggested by the phrase translated "sat at the Lord's feet." Not only is Mary neglecting "women's work," but she is also taking on a male role.[1]

5. Who is Martha upset with?

6. How would you describe Martha's tone when she speaks to Jesus? What does she sound like?

7. What phrases reveal Martha's self-centeredness?

8. How might Martha have loved Mary instead of judging her?

Insight: The Problem of Legalism

When we see what love is, we can see that Martha's appeal to justice is a mask for selfishness. Legalism focuses on a rule and forgets about the person. The rule isn't bad, but our selfishness uses it as a weapon. Martha can't think about Mary's world because she's only thinking about her own work and rules.

---

[1] "To sit at the feet of a respected rabbi was the position of a disciple. In Acts 22:3, Paul says he was instructed 'at the feet of Gamaliel' (NRSV), a leading rabbi of Jerusalem (cf. Luke 8:35)…Mary's initiative in taking this position is particularly shocking, since rabbis did not have women disciples." Mark Strauss, "Luke" in *Zondervan Illustrated Bible Backgrounds Commentary: Volume 1*. Ed. Clinton E. Arnold. (Grand Rapids, MI: Zondervan, 2002), 417.

SECTION 2: Judas' Legalism — 10 mins

John 12:1-8—Mary Anointing Jesus with Perfume

[1] Six days before the Passover, Jesus came to Bethany, where Lazarus lived, whom Jesus had raised from the dead. [2] Here a dinner was given in Jesus' honor. Martha served, while Lazarus was among those reclining at the table with him. [3] Then Mary took about a pint of pure nard, an expensive perfume; she poured it on Jesus' feet and wiped his feet with her hair. And the house was filled with the fragrance of the perfume.

[4] But one of his disciples, Judas Iscariot, who was later to betray him, objected, [5] "Why wasn't this perfume sold and the money given to the poor? It was worth a year's wages." [6] He did not say this because he cared about the poor but because he was a thief; as keeper of the money bag, he used to help himself to what was put into it.

[7] "Leave her alone," Jesus replied. "It was intended that she should save this perfume for the day of my burial. [8] You will always have the poor among you, but you will not always have me."

Historical Background: Dowry

"A year's wages" is about 300 denarii or, very roughly, about $30,000 today. Very possibly, this is Mary's dowry, the property or money a bride brings into marriage. In the ancient world and in some parts of the world today, a dowry is required for marriage. So, this represents more than Mary's life savings; she is cashing in her ticket to marriage, children, and acceptance in society.

9. What similarities can we observe about Mary and Martha compared to when we last saw them?

10. To Judas, what good principle is Mary violating?

11. What was Judas' real motivation in rebuking Mary?

Mark 14:10-11

[10] Then Judas Iscariot, one of the Twelve, went to the chief priests to betray Jesus to them. [11] They were delighted to hear this and promised to give him money. So he watched for an opportunity to hand him over.

12. What does Judas do right after Jesus rebukes him?

13. How is Judas' rebuke of Mary dishonest?

SECTION 3: Our Legalism — 5 mins

Illustration: Family Entertainment (Paul Miller)

Paul Miller shares this story from the days before streaming video: "We were pretty tight financially, and I had saved a little money on the side. We had rented a video for the night and when the time came to take it back my wife wanted me to pay for it out of my money. I resented that and argued with her about who should pay the $3.00 rental. My rule was: costs of Miller family video rentals should be shared equally. Later, I realized that by arguing with her, I was communicating she had less value than the price of a video rental. (I also remembered that I had agreed to pay for the movie out of my stash.) I took a good principle—'you should share'—and used it for selfish ends. The result was I hurt my wife."[2]

Illustration: Spilled Water (Libbie Groves in response to Paul's story above.)

"My behavior shows that sometimes I treat people as less important than the price of a video rental. Here is an example: When my youngest daughter broke or spilled or wasted something I stopped and asked myself, 'Is she less important than water all over the floor? Or a broken cup? Or a bowl of soggy cereal? Or the time to clean up the mess?' That helped me not to get upset. It wasn't that I simply masked my irritation better or pretended to be [a] kind parent, etc., but I really wasn't even irked, because I saw the issue in terms of 'what is more valuable—my daughter or the object in question?'"[3]

---

[2] Paul Miller, *Love Walked Among Us* (Colorado Springs, CO: NavPress, 2001), 64.

[3] Private conversation with Libbie Groves, Glenside, PA.

14. Can you think of a time when someone related to you on the basis of his or her rules and forgot about you as a person? Describe what happened. What was the rule? How did you feel?

15. Ask yourself, "What rules do I have that, at times, become legalistic?"

SECTION 4: Idols 15 mins

Romans 1:21-23

> [21] For although they knew God, they neither glorified him as God nor gave thanks to him, but their thinking became futile and their foolish hearts were darkened. [22] Although they claimed to be wise, they became fools [23] and exchanged the glory of the immortal God for images made to look like a mortal human being and birds and animals and reptiles.

16. According to Romans, what happens to people when they don't give glory to God?

Insight:
Scripture tells us that when we don't worship God, we will invariably worship something else in God's creation—money, fame, sex, pleasure, vacations, etc. This is called idolatry.

PERSON	IDOL	HOW IDOL SHAPES BEHAVIOR
Martha		
Judas		
Mary		
You		

17. Thinking back to the stories we've discussed, what is Martha's life organized around? What's important to her?

18. What is Judas' life organized around?

19. What is Mary's life organized around?

20. What kind of behavior does Martha's idolatry lead to?

21. What kind of behavior does Judas' idolatry lead to?

22. What kind of behavior does Mary's worship lead to?

Gospel Connection:

Idolatry: The Bible teaches that idolatry leads to sexual perversion and the destruction of relationships (Romans 1:24-32). The root problem with our personal relationships is that our relationship with God is out of sync. Restoring our relationship with God begins the process of restoring our relationship with people. (In effect, Jesus says the same thing when he tells Simon, "He who has been forgiven much, loves much and he who has been forgiven little, loves little.") If the vertical connection (God) is out of whack, then the horizontal connection (people) will be marred as well.

An Idol Changes Us: An idol changes us. Psalm 115:8 says, "Those who make [idols] will be like them, and so will all who trust in them." (See also Psalm 135:18.) We become like the idols we worship. For example, if you are captured by the idol of appearance, you will spend lots of time trying to look beautiful. You will judge people when you think they look bad. In the end, your heart will be neglected as you pursue your idols, and you will become as shallow as the idol itself.

23. What do you center your life around?

SECTION 5: The Peculiar Blindness of the Legalist 5 mins

THE ACCUSATION	HOW DO THEY DO THE SAME THING?
Martha: Mary is wasting time; Jesus doesn't care.	
Judas: Mary is wasting money.	
Simon: Jesus is blind to the sinful woman.	

Romans 2:1

"You, therefore, have no excuse, you who pass judgment on someone else, for at whatever point you judge the other, you are condemning yourself, because you who pass judgment do the same things."

24. Are Martha, Judas, and Simon aware of their blindness?

LESSON 9 APPLICATION

1. What did the Spirit help you see about either Jesus or yourself through this lesson?

2. Recall a time that someone related to you on the basis of his or her rules and forgot about you as a person. Describe what happened. What was the rule? How did you feel?

3. Ask yourself, "What rules do I have that, at times, become legalistic?"

4. Let's dig a little deeper. Make a list of things that bug you about other people. Keep the list in front of you and prayerfully ask yourself the question, "Do I do any of these things?" You might not do exactly the same things. For instance, the Pharisees didn't commit adultery, but they looked at women lustfully (Matthew 5:21-48). Jot down connections between your list and your behavior. Then, if you really want to get a read on yourself, ask one or two people who know you well, "Do I do any of these things?"

5. Reflect on the chart on page 106. What do you center your life around? How does that shape your behavior?

6. What did you learn about yourself in answering these questions? How is the Spirit prompting you to respond?

LESSON 10: INCARNATION

OUTLINE:

1. Incarnation Goes Inside . . . . 10 mins
2. Two Gospel Scenes—We Witness Jesus Incarnate. . . . . 15 mins
3. The Golden Rule—Jesus Invites Us to Incarnate . . . . 10 mins
4. A Culture of Self . . . . 5 mins
5. Who Will Make the First Move? . . . . 5 mins

LESSON 10: INCARNATION

SECTION 1: Incarnation Goes Inside 10 mins

1. Do we prefer to ask questions or tell people what to do? Why?

Mark 10:46-52—Jesus and Blind Bartimaeus

[46] Then they came to Jericho. As Jesus and his disciples, together with a large crowd, were leaving the city, a blind man, Bartimaeus (which means "son of Timaeus"), was sitting by the roadside begging. [47] When he heard that it was Jesus of Nazareth, he began to shout, "Jesus, Son of David, have mercy on me!"

[48] Many rebuked him and told him to be quiet, but he shouted all the more, "Son of David, have mercy on me!"

[49] Jesus stopped and said, "Call him."

So they called to the blind man, "Cheer up! On your feet! He's calling you." [50] Throwing his cloak aside, he jumped to his feet and came to Jesus.

[51] "What do you want me to do for you?" Jesus asked him.

The blind man said, "Rabbi, I want to see."

[52] "Go," said Jesus, "your faith has healed you." Immediately he received his sight and followed Jesus along the road.

Historical Background: Son of David

By calling Jesus "son of David," Bartimaeus recognizes Jesus as royalty, since David was an ancient king in Israel.

Historical Background: Jericho

- Jericho is where the Good Samaritan began his journey to Jerusalem.
- It is an oasis on the southern end of the Jordan River.
- Jericho, called the "City of Palms," is one of the oldest continually inhabited cities—dating back to 6,000 B.C.

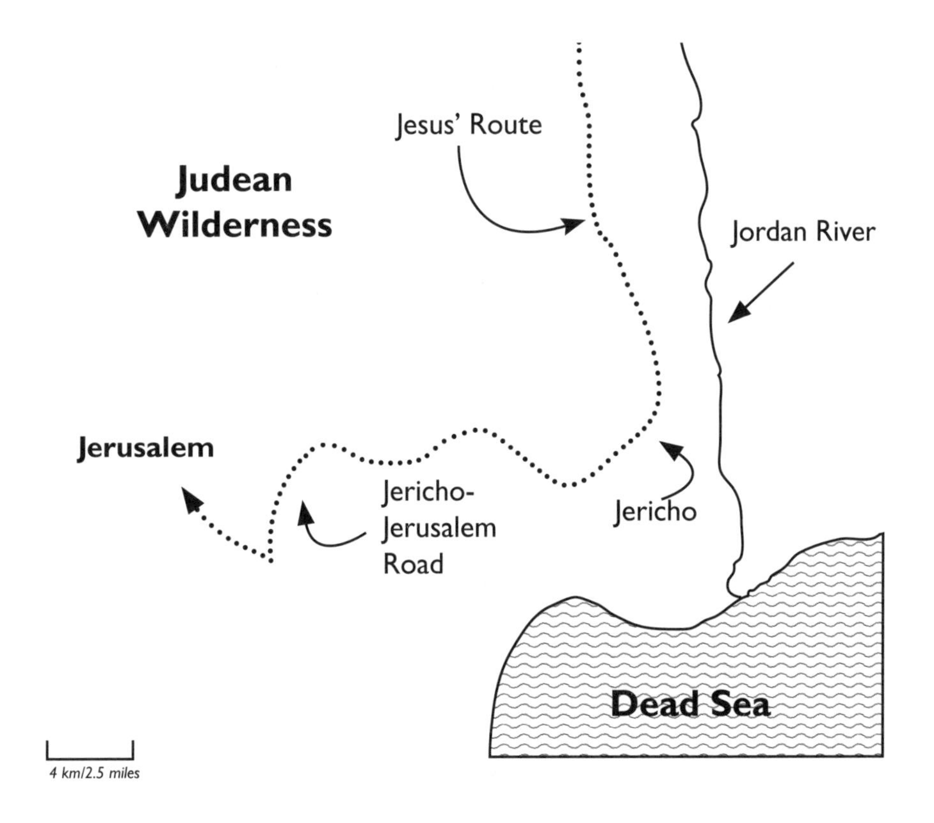

2. **Which is faster: asking a question first or just healing the man?**

3. **What is strange about Jesus asking Bartimaeus, "What do you want me to do for you?"**

4. **What is good about Jesus' question? How might it affect Bartimaeus?**

5. Who or what is at the center of this miracle?

Insight: Paternalism, the Opposite of Incarnation

- *Incarnation* seeks to go inside of others to find out what their needs are, as opposed to standing on the outside and helping them. When I incarnate with you, I slow down and think about your world. No one can help me think more clearly about your world than you.
- *Paternalism* is an attitude of being above other people when we help. We feel good because we've done a good deed, but the other person feels not only our good deed but also our lack of understanding.

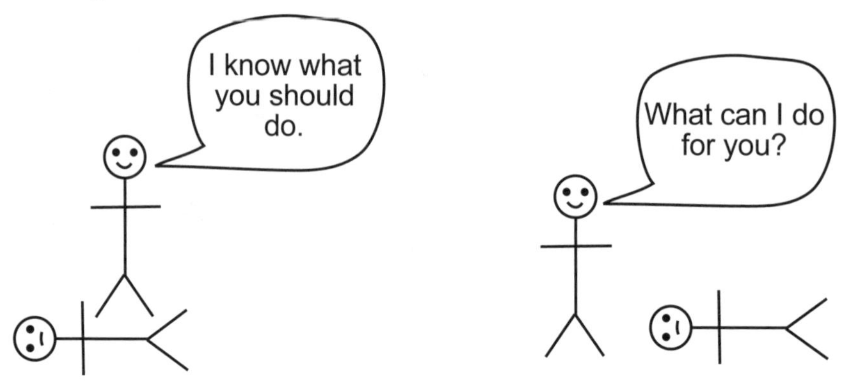

6. Why is it scary to ask someone Jesus' question: "What can I do for you?"

7. What can be exciting about asking, "What can I do for you?"

Gospel Connection:

Jesus moving toward Bartimaeus and answering his cry for mercy is a small example of the pattern of incarnation that characterized Jesus' life and death. The early church expanded the cry of Bartimaeus to create what is now called "The Jesus Prayer": "Lord Jesus Christ, Son of David, have mercy on me, a sinner." "The Jesus Prayer" is a simple description of faith. The "Jesus Question,"—"What can I do for you?"—is a simple description of love.

SECTION 2: Two Gospel Scenes—We Witness Jesus Incarnate 15 mins

Story #1: Mark 8:1-4—Feeding of the 4,000

[1] During those days another large crowd gathered. Since they had nothing to eat, Jesus called his disciples to him and said, [2] "I have compassion for these people; they have already been with me three days and have nothing to eat. [3] If I send them home hungry, they will collapse on the way, because some of them have come a long distance."

[4] His disciples answered, "But where in this remote place can anyone get enough bread to feed them?"

Historical Background: Decapolis

This scene takes place southeast of the Sea of Galilee in a region called the Decapolis—so named because it has ten cities in it. It is a Gentile region, and Jews did not generally have contact with or concern for Gentiles.

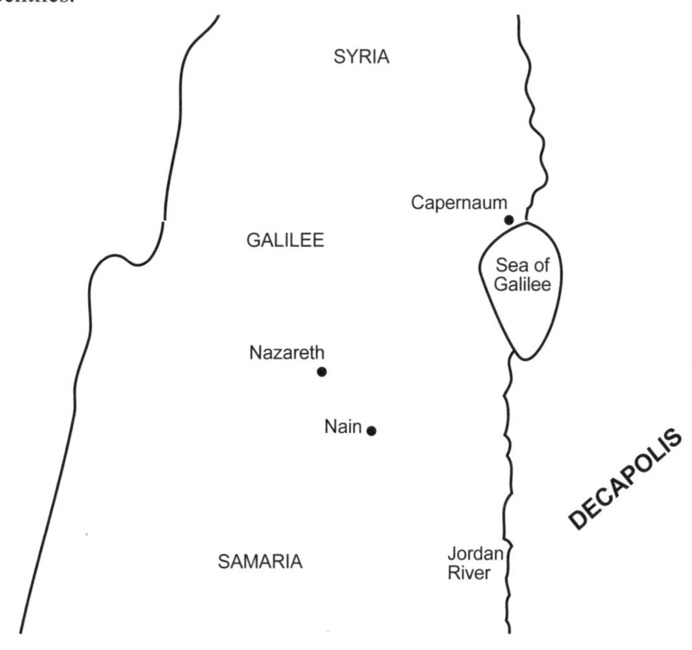

8. In verses 1 to 3, what four clear facts does Jesus observe about the people?

9. Why mention these things? Are they not obvious? What is Jesus doing here?

Insight: Incarnating

Jesus' comments are mundane. We could read right by them, thinking of them as only an introduction to a miracle. We expect that Jesus will always have something "deep" or "mystical" to say. A follower of God should be floating above life. We assume that if we knew what Jesus was thinking, it would be deep, but it's so simple, so plain. Jesus' mundane comments are a small incarnation. The Latin root of incarnation is "in" + "carnes" ("flesh"—as in "carnivore"). It literally means "in [someone's] flesh."

10. Why do you think Jesus is going out of his way to show his disciples what compassion looks like with this particular group of people?

Story #2: Matthew 9:36

"And seeing the multitudes, he felt compassion for them, because they were distressed [harassed] and helpless [thrown down] like sheep without a shepherd."

11. What kind of needs is Jesus looking at here?

Insight:

- Love always looks at both the physical and spiritual needs of a person.
- The word translated "helpless" literally means "thrown down." If sheep are on their backs or they turn the wrong way, they will simply get stuck because they are so dumb.

- "Sheep without a shepherd" highlights the inability of sheep to be alone. We hear about wild cats, dogs, goats, and cattle, but we never hear about wild sheep. They cannot survive on their own.

SECTION 3: The Golden Rule—Jesus Invites Us to Incarnate 10 mins

Insight: The Golden Rule is actually a guide for incarnation.

- "So in everything, do to others what you would have them do to you, for this sums up the Law and the Prophets" (Matthew 7:12).
- "Do to others as you would have them do to you" (Luke 6:31).

12. What two things do you have to do to follow the Golden Rule?

13. Why does Jesus want us to reflect before we love?

14. How do you start reflecting about someone's life?

Insight: the Golden Rule and Incarnation

- The Golden Rule is a guide to incarnation. We move into another's world by considering what it would be like to be in that world.
- This is what Jesus is doing when he looks out on the crowd. "They have been with me for three days…."
- The heart of the Golden Rule is understanding other people. It is something we all want from others, yet we are slow to do it ourselves.
- At its simplest, incarnation is slowing down and asking questions even when the situation seems obvious—i.e., "My wife is grumpy this evening. I wonder if something's wrong. Let me find out how her day was."

SECTION 4: A Culture of Self 5 mins

15. What modern phrases do we read in self-help books or on social media about how we should relate to ourselves?

16. How are these phrases different from the Golden Rule?

17. Think about the phrase "learn to love yourself." The phrase assumes we don't love ourselves. How is that different from the assumption of the Golden Rule?

Insight: Self-Absorption

- Jesus' words were as opposed to his culture as they are to ours. Our culture is self-absorbed. It has made the worship of self the centerpiece of personal religion.
- Self-absorption is evil. Referring to killers and sociopaths, Dr. Carl Bell, a psychiatrist at the University of Illinois, said, "They cannot see the self in the other."[1] The Bible says evil is self-deification, ignoring the true God and making ourselves into little gods.
- Total self-absorption always leads to insanity. For example, the Lost Son "came to himself" when he was out in the pigsty—implying that he had not been in his right mind (Luke 15:17).

SECTION 5: Who Will Make the First Move? 5 mins

18. If you are always seeking to understand others, who is going to take the time to understand you? Is it ever okay to just take care of yourself?

[1] Carl Bell (*Newsweek*, May 21, 2001), 32.

Gospel Connection:

- The Gospels show us how to love, but their main point is not to give us a road map of love; it's to show us that incarnation is how God loves us. He understands us. His mind is full of us. By sending his Son Jesus into the world, God has literally incarnated with us. So, no matter how others fail to care for us, we always have God; like the Father in the Parable of the Lost Son, he's watching for us to come home.
- At Pentecost, fifty days after his resurrection, Jesus again entered human flesh, but this time it was through the Holy Spirit coming into his people. The Spirit brings the very person of Jesus into our lives. We don't have to love on our own. Jesus within us does the loving.

19. How do you want others to respond when you are going through a difficult time? How do you think others want you to respond when they are struggling?

Insight:

Jesus faced this situation on the cross. As he was dying, the high priests mocked him saying, "He saved others; he cannot save himself" (Matthew 27:42). This is precisely our fear in incarnating with others. If we are always seeking to rescue other people, who will rescue us when the time comes? Jesus was utterly alone, and his incarnation resulted in suffering. But because he endured being alone, we don't have to be alone. When we believe in his incarnation for us, which led to his death, we are given power to incarnate with others, which will also lead to death—death of our will. Now the presence of the Holy Spirit is proof we are not alone, and that gives us confidence to incarnate, even when no one wants to understand us.

Insight:

In the next unit of *Person of Jesus* (starting with lesson 12), we'll see that Jesus does more than understand people; he is also honest with them. Many times, he speaks hard words that help us understand ourselves.

LESSON 10 APPLICATION

1. What did the Spirit help you see about either Jesus or yourself through this lesson?

2. Thinking back to the two crowd scenes discussed in this lesson, what strikes you most about Jesus' behavior? Why?

3. Share with the group a time someone incarnated with you. How did that change your thoughts, feelings, or even your situation?

4. Reflect for a minute on a situation when you wish someone had taken the time to understand your world. What difference might incarnation have made?

5. Recall a time when the Spirit enabled you to incarnate with someone else. What happened? How did it change you or the other person?

Read this brief illustration from Paul Miller's life:

> In order to understand this story you need to understand that I like to save money. At one point in my life I thought it was just frugality. But as I have gotten older, I have to frankly admit it is not a virtue, but something that I enjoy for its own sake. I feel good when I find the exact change for the toll collector, and I don't have to break a five-dollar bill. There is a sense of inner peace that comes over me when I take my daughter's report card into Blockbuster to get a free movie. The amount of money is not crucial. It just feels good.
>
> I was cheering on my 17-year-old daughter, Ashley, at her hockey game. She played very hard in her halfback position, working up a tremendous thirst. As my daughter came off the field, I congratulated her warmly. She said to me, "I am so thirsty, Dad, could you get me a soda?"
>
> My mind immediately went to the large supply of ice water reserved for the players. I thought of mentioning it, but then I thought of how Jesus loves by putting himself in someone else's shoes. I could do that with Ashley. I thought to myself, "I have money in my pocket. I could spend that money. I could walk over to the soda machine 200 yards away in the school building and get a soda for Ashley." I thought that simply. I know it sounds silly, but I am not naturally compassionate. I need to break down each step, one step at a time.
>
> So, I went for the soda. As I trudged off in the heat leaving the free, ice-cold water behind, I thought of the look on Ashley's face when she would see me come back with a soda. I thought of the simple statement it would imprint on her heart: "My dad loves me." I thought of the most basic movement of love: compassion leads to oneness or closeness.[2]

6. What initially prevented Paul from incarnating with his daughter?

7. How did Paul put himself in his daughter's shoes? What did that lead him to do?

---

[2] Paul Miller, *Love Walked Among Us*, 67-68.

8. Brainstorm a short list of preferences and rules that Paul had to "put to death" in this situation in order to love his daughter in this way.

9. Whom do you find it most difficult to incarnate with? Why? What preferences and rules might you need to put to death, by the Spirit, in order to incarnate with this person?

LESSON 11: INCARNATION CHANGES US

OUTLINE:

1. Review: The Theme of Incarnation. . . . . 10 mins
2. What Incarnation Does to Us. . . . . 10 mins
3. What Jesus' Incarnation Does for Us. . . . . 10 mins
4. Imitating Jesus' Incarnation . . . . 15 mins

LESSON 11: INCARNATION CHANGES US

SECTION 1: Review—The Theme of Incarnation 10 mins

1. **How do you see Jesus incarnating with the widow in Luke 7:12-15?**

2. **How does the Good Samaritan incarnate with the man on the Jericho road in Luke 10:30-35? How does he apply the Golden Rule?**

3. **How well do the disciples incarnate with the blind man in John 9:1-7? In what ways does Jesus incarnate with him?**

4. **Why is Simon the Pharisee in Luke 7:36-50 unable to incarnate with the adulterous woman who crashed his party?**

5. **Why is Simon unable to incarnate with Jesus?**

6. **How does Jesus, on the other hand, incarnate with the woman?**

7. **How does Jesus incarnate with Simon?**

8. How does Jesus help Simon incarnate?

SECTION 2: What Incarnation Does to Us — 10 mins

9. What's the difference between studying unemployment (for example, doing a research paper in school) and being unemployed?

10. If you were unemployed, would you rather turn to a friend who has been unemployed or a friend who has never been unemployed? Why?

Illustration: An Unemployed Person

If you see an unemployed person, you might judge him, thinking, "That would never happen to me," or, "I wonder what he did that made him lose his job." But if you become unemployed, you begin to understand. You no longer judge. In fact, you're sympathetic to the plight of the unemployed. This is what Jesus did for us, except that he never judged us. This example shows why incarnation is so crucial to love. Unless we get into the other person's shoes—either through experience or by taking the time to understand him or her—we will love poorly. (We need not have experienced exactly the same struggle, but then we need to labor to listen, to understand the other person's world.) Incarnation changes us.

Hebrews 4:15; 5:2

[15] For we do not have a high priest who is unable to sympathize with our weaknesses, but we have one who has been tempted in every way, just as we are—yet was without sin.

---

[2] He is able to deal gently with those who are ignorant and are going astray, since he himself is subject to weakness.

Insight:

- In heaven with the Father, Jesus never knew hunger, pain, or loneliness. He was fully love, but he had never tasted those things.
- When Jesus slows down to look, feel compassion, and act, it is a mini-incarnation. Sharing in people's humanity = incarnating.
- Jesus became perfect through his incarnation; he became a complete Savior.
- It's a mystery how Jesus was made complete by suffering when he was already perfect.[1] It's not a mystery with us, though. Being unemployed makes us more compassionate for the unemployed!

Principle: Walking in someone's shoes shapes and changes us.

Henri Nouwen

"Compassion is hard because it requires the inner disposition to go with others to the place where they are weak, vulnerable, lonely, and broken. But this is not our spontaneous response to suffering. What we desire most is to do away with suffering by fleeing from it or finding a quick cure for it. … We want to…[do] something to show that our presence makes a difference. So we ignore our greatest gift, which is our ability to enter into solidarity with those who suffer."[2]

Illustration: In the Water
A missionary translator was translating the Bible for a tribe in Southeast Asia. They told him that the word for "love" was "pa." But "pa" didn't seem to capture the idea of self-sacrificial love portrayed in the Bible. One day while the translator was crossing a swollen stream on a raft with two native women, the raft overturned. At the risk of his own life, he rescued the two women. The tribesmen described what he had done as "che." The difference between "che" and "pa" is that "che" means to be down with the people whom you are helping. "Pa" means to help from a safe position. When Jesus became a man, he was in the water, risking himself to save us.[3]

11. How did the missionary translator learn compassion?

---

[1] God was driven into our world by who he is—pure love. The character of God inevitably leads to a manger in Bethlehem. Dr. Todd Mangum, Professor of Theology at Biblical Seminary, puts it this way: "It's not that Jesus was previously 'unaware' of what was involved in having to do something one does not want to have to do—He had seen that done by Abraham, Moses, Jonah, Jeremiah, Samuel, et al. for millennia. But 'from a distance,' as it were. He had never had to actually do it before—this doing it for the first time the writer of Hebrews calls, appropriately, 'learning.'" Dr. Todd Mangum. "Christ as High Priest." Lecture, Theology IV: Church and Consummation, from Biblical Theological Seminary, Hatfield, PA: Spring 1999.

[2] Henri J.M. Nouwen, *The Way of the Heart* (San Francisco: Harper San Francisco, 1991), 34.

[3] Jack Miller, from sermon at New Life Presbyterian Church, Glenside, PA, 1982.

SECTION 3: What Jesus' Incarnation Does for Us — 10 mins

Hebrews 2:14

Since the children have flesh and blood, he too shared in their humanity so that by his death he might destroy him who holds the power of death….

Hebrews 2:17-18

[17] For this reason he had to be made like his brothers in every way, in order that he might become a merciful and faithful high priest in service to God, and that he might make atonement for the sins of the people. [18] Because he himself suffered when tempted, he is able to help those who are being tempted.

12. What does it mean that Jesus was "made like his brothers"?

13. What's the difference between "getting in touch with myself" and being "made like his brothers"?

The Man in the Pit[4]

Imagine a man who has fallen into a pit—a deep, filthy pit with a venomous snake that he's desperately trying to avoid. Along comes an Animist (representing tribal religions), who looks down into the pit and sees the snake. His eyes open wide, and he flees into the jungle before the same evil spirit can throw him into the pit. Then, along comes the Confucianist, who says, "You should have been more careful. If you had been looking where you were going, you would not have fallen into the pit." (Confucianism is simply a moral code. It doesn't provide a savior other than praying to one's ancestors.)

The Hindu comes along and says, "Ah, you think that you are in a great black pit, but that is the error of mortal mind. The fact is that all is Brahman and Brahman is all and this external world is merely illusion. The pit does not exist. Think, 'There is no pit, there is no pit, there is no serpent, and all will be well... peace.'"

Then a Muslim sees the man in the pit and says, "It is easy to get out of the pit, my friend. Just practice the five truths of Islam: Give alms to the poor, make a pilgrimage to Mecca, pray five times a day toward Mecca, fast during the month of Ramadan, and confess, 'There is one God, Allah, and Mohammed is his prophet.'" Then comes the Buddhist who looks down and says, "Dear friend, you are suffering greatly in that pit, and the reason you are suffering is that you want to get out of the pit. It is your desire that is making you miserable. What you must come to is a cessation of all desire, and then you won't mind being in the pit."

And then Jesus comes and looks with compassionate eyes at the man in the pit, and into that foul and filthy pit he leaps between the man and the serpent—who strikes at Jesus, sinking his fangs into his side. As the venom flows into Jesus, he lifts that man out of the pit.[5]

14. How is Christianity's view of the man in the pit different from that of other religions?

15. What does Jesus do that none of the other would-be helpers did?

16. Many tried to help the man in the pit, but only one could actually rescue him. Reflect briefly on the ways—apart from Jesus—you've tried to escape the pit. What happened?

17. How have you sensed Jesus "in the pit" with you?

---

[4] This parable shows the logical consequences of religious belief. (But individual Muslims or Buddhists might not act in the ways described in this parable.) For instance, Buddhist philosophy really believes that the problem of human suffering is caused by our desires. Because we believe this world is real, we are in constant tension with it. The only solution for the Buddhist is to reach Nirvana, the state of being absorbed in the all-soul and ceasing to exist as an individual. Different religions are not different ways to God; they are radically different ways of viewing reality.

[5] Adapted from D. James Kennedy, *Truths That Transform* (Fleming H. Revell Company, 1974), 59.

SECTION 4: Imitating Jesus' Incarnation 15 mins

Excerpts from Sermon by B.B. Warfield—Philippians 2:1-11[6]

There is no length to which Christ's self-sacrifice did not lead Him...God took such thought for us, that He made no account of Himself. Into the immeasurable calm of the divine blessedness He permitted this thought to enter, "I will die for men!" And so mighty was His love, so colossal the divine purpose to save, that He thought nothing of His divine majesty, nothing of His unsullied blessedness, nothing of His equality with God, but, absorbed in us—our needs, our misery, our helplessness—He made no account of Himself.

If this is to be our example, what limit can we set to our self-sacrifice? Let us remember that we are no longer our own but Christ's, bought with the price of His precious blood, and are now to live, not for ourselves but for Him—serving Him in serving them. Let all thought of our dignity, our possessions, our rights, perish out of sight, when Christ's service calls. Let the mind be in us that was also in Him, when He took no account of Himself, but, God as He was, took the lowly obedience even unto death, and that the death of the cross. In such a mind as this, where is the end of unselfishness?

...Self-sacrifice means not indifference to our times and our fellows: it means absorption in them. It means forgetfulness of self in others. It means entering into every person's hopes and fears, longings and despairs: it means many sidedness of spirit, multiform activity, multiplicity of sympathies. It means richness of development. It means not that we should live one life, but a thousand lives—binding ourselves to a thousand souls by the filaments of so loving a sympathy that their lives become ours....

Only, when, like Christ, and in loving obedience to His call and example, we take no account of ourselves, but freely give ourselves to others, we shall find the saying true of himself also: "Wherefore also God has highly exalted him." The path of self-sacrifice is the path to glory.

18. How do you feel after hearing this?

19. How can we love this way?

[6] Excerpted and edited from Warfield, *The Person and Work of Christ*, 572-575.

LESSON 11 APPLICATION

1. What did the Spirit help you see about either Jesus or yourself through this lesson?

2. Find a quiet place and carve out some time to reflect on the Jesus stories you've studied in this unit. Which one moves your heart most profoundly? What does it show you about Jesus? About yourself? Enjoy an extended time of worship as you journal your answers to these questions.

3. What themes have emerged (such as self-righteousness, legalism, looking, etc.) as areas where the Spirit might be calling you to respond? What might that response look like in the coming days, weeks, or months?

4. In what ways do you know and love Jesus now that you did not know and love him at the beginning of this study?

5. The next unit of this study focuses on honesty. What questions do you have about Jesus' honesty? Jot those down now as you anticipate how God will answer them.

LESSON 11 ADDENDUM

Naturalism vs. Theism

Is it possible that Jesus, as God, became man?

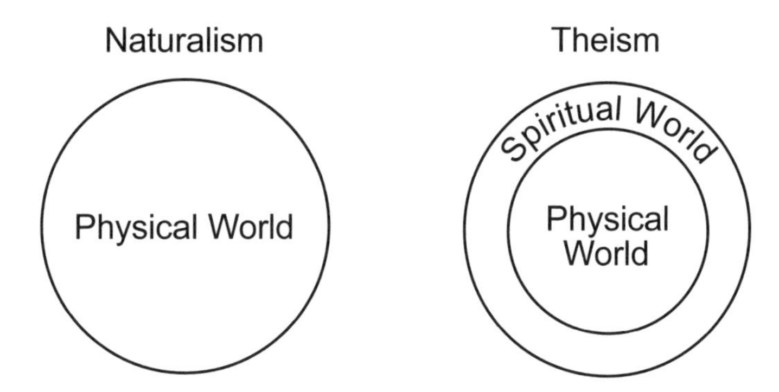

Insight: Naturalism vs. Theism

- Naturalism is a system of belief. Naturalism is a belief that the world we see is all that exists. It is a statement of faith that God doesn't exist. It is faith because there's no evidence to prove it. No one can prove that God doesn't exist. Science recognizes the existence of many phenomena that we can't observe directly. We can see only their reflections. Naturalism is a remarkable statement of faith because, for the entire history of mankind, there is no evidence that any culture did not believe in some aspect of the spiritual world.
- Naturalism's foundation rests not on science—that is, the study of the physical world—but on the theory of evolution. *Darwin's Black Box* by Michael Behe and *Darwin on Trial* by Philip Johnson are excellent critiques of evolution; they're scholarly books, not given to polemics or overstatement. As Johnson writes, Darwin himself observed that the "biggest problem with his theory of evolution is the fossil record."[7] Usually people assume fossil evidence proves the theory of evolution. Darwin's theory predicts a gradual change in species and a gradual emerging of new species. When Darwin wrote *On the Origin of Species*, the fossil record didn't show those gradations, but instead revealed clearly defined species. Stephen Jay Gould, a leading paleontologist at Harvard, has admitted that the evidence is still not there.[8]

---

[7] Philip Johnson, *Darwin on Trial* (Downers Grove, IL: IVP, 1993), 46-47.

[8] Johnson, *Darwin on Trial*, 50.

- Science rightly says that magic doesn't exist. Magic is an arbitrary suspension of the laws of nature. It is irrational. But science doesn't deal with the issue of a spiritual world intersecting the physical. That would be comparable to a football player trying to tell a design engineer how to design the dome of a stadium.
- Incarnation is miracle, not magic. It is God coming out of his larger circle to dwell in the smaller circle—a movement of humility.

About

seeJesus is a global discipling mission passionate about equipping the worldwide church to reflect all the beauty of Jesus. We invite you to learn more about our books, Bible studies, and seminars:

Subscribe at info@seejesus.net

Listen at seeJesus.net/podcast

@_PaulEMiller

Facebook/seeJesus.net